MW00807621

Cooperative Learning

Science

High School Activities

Michael Michels
Angela Manzi
Janina Mele

Kagan

©2003 **Kagan Publishing**

This book is published by **Kagan Publishing**. All rights are reserved by **Kagan Publishing**. No part of this publication may be reproduced or transmitted in any form by any means, electronic or mechanical, including photocopy, recording, or any information storage and retrieval system, without prior written permission from **Kagan Publishing**. The blackline masters may be duplicated only by classroom teachers who purchase the book and only for use in their own classrooms. To obtain additional copies of this book, other **Kagan** publications or information regarding professional development, contact **Kagan**.

Kagan Publishing
981 Calle Amanecer
San Clemente, CA 92673
1 (800) 933-2667
Fax: (949) 545-6301
www.KaganOnline.com

ISBN: 978-1-879097-74-2

Table of Contents

STRUCTURES FOR SCIENCE

Table of Contents Cont.

Chart of Structures

 General Science
 Physical Science
 Earth Science
 Chemistry
 Biology

Structures	General Science		Physical Science		Earth Science		Chemistry		Biology	
	Activity Ideas	Blacklines	Activity Ideas	Blacklines	Activity Ideas	Blacklines	Activity Ideas	Blacklines	Activity Ideas	Blacklines
Find Someone Who	N/A	22	18	20	14	16	10	12	6	8
Pairs Check	46	48	42	44	38	40	34	36	30	32
Corners	96	N/A	86	88	75	77	64	66	52	54
Mix-N-Match	150	152	138	140	126	128	114	116	100	104
Word Webbing	178	179	172	174	168	170	162	164	156	158
Give One–Get One	N/A	202	198	200	194	196	190	192	186	188

Biology

Activities

Find Someone Who

Activity Ideas

Blacklines

Pairs Check

Activity Ideas

Blacklines

Corners

Activity Ideas

Blacklines

Mix-N-Match

Activity Ideas

Blackline

& Blacklines

Word Webbing

Give One–Get One

More Structures

Agree-Disagree Line-Ups

Fan-N-Pick

Numbered Heads Together

Sequencing

Showdown

Telephone

Timed Pair Share

Chemistry
Activities

Find Someone Who

Activity Ideas

Blacklines

Pairs Check

Activity Ideas

Blacklines

Corners

Activity Ideas

Blacklines

Mix-N-Match

Activity Ideas

Blackline

& B l a c k l i n e s

Kagan Publishing • 1 (800) 933-2667
www.KaganOnline.com

Earth Science
A c t i v i t i e s

Find Someone Who
Activity Ideas

Blacklines

Pairs Check
Activity Ideas

Blacklines

Corners
Activity Ideas

Blacklines

Mix-N-Match
Activity Ideas

Blacklines

Kagan Publishing • 1 (800) 933-2667
www.KaganOnline.com

Cooperative Learning Activities For High School Science

& **B l a c k l i n e s**

Word Webbing

Give One–Get One

More Structures

Agree-Disagree Line-Ups

Fan-N-Pick

Mix-Freeze-Group

Sequencing

Showdown

Telephone

Timed Pair Share

Physical Science
Activities

Find Someone Who

Activity Ideas

Blacklines

Pairs Check

Activity Ideas

Blacklines

Corners

Activity Ideas

Blacklines

Mix-N-Match

Activity Ideas

Blackline

& B l a c k l i n e s

Word Webbing

Activity Ideas

Blacklines

Give One–Get One

Activity Ideas

Blacklines

More Structures

Agree-Disagree Line-Ups

Fan-N-Pick

Mix-Freeze-Group

Sequencing

Showdown

Telephone

Timed Pair Share

General Science
A c t i v i t i e s

& Blacklines

Foreword

By Dr. Spencer Kagan

For a number of years, those of us who were pioneering the cooperative learning movement in the United States observed and puzzled over an anomaly. The extensive research on cooperative learning revealed that academic achievement gains were as large and as consistent among high school students as among elementary school students, yet implementation of cooperative learning was far greater at the elementary level. A large scale meta-analysis involving hundreds of research studies revealed no difference in the effectiveness of cooperative learning for high school vs. elementary school students — for all students, large, consistent gains in academic and social variables were found.[1] It just was not logical: Logic would dictate that if the evidence in support of cooperative learning was equally strong for elementary and secondary, implementation should also be equally strong. But for quite a number of years, cooperative learning flourished at the elementary school level and languished at the high school level.

It was only belatedly that we realized the problem resided in the resources and trainings we were offering. Those of us who were developing the field of cooperative learning were developing generic cooperative learning methods, but in our workshops and books we never specifically outlined how to apply those methods to understanding the periodic table, the layers of the earth, the difference between speed and velocity, macromolecules, or the nature of a DNA helix. This book, *Cooperative Learning and Science: High School Activities*, goes a long way to remedy that deficit.

Cooperative Learning and Science: High School Activities follows a recent tradition begun in 1998 with the publication of Tom Morton's *Cooperative Learning & Social Studies*.[2] When that book was published, we were flabbergasted. Almost immediately, the book became one of Kagan Publishing's best sellers. High school teachers were saying, *"Finally a book just for me."* We followed Morton's publication with two books for high school math: Dina Kushnir wrote Cooperative Learning & Mathematics: High School Activities[3] and Becky Bride wrote Cooperative Learning & High School Geometry.[4] In each case, the response exceeded our expectations. High school teachers were clamoring for cooperative learning resources.

Today, our secondary workshops are now just as popular as our elementary workshops. Secondary teachers are responding to the workshops with unbridled enthusiasm, "Finally a workshop just for me!" Demand for cooperative learning trainings and resources among high school and college professors now rivals the demand among elementary school teachers.

Why Has Cooperative Learning Come to High School?

What happened to account for this shift? What brought cooperative learning to high school? I can offer six explanations: 1) Students are carrying the cooperative learning message; 2) Students are different today; 3) Employability skills are shifting; 4) Block scheduling; 5) Resources are becoming available; 6) Structures.

Students Carry a Message. A number of years ago, I began doing large district-wide trainings. A pattern emerged. First, we would be called to train the elementary school teachers. A few years later, we would get a call to train the middle school teachers. Then, a few years later, we would get another phone call. This time it was a request to train the high school teachers. What was happening? A few years after we trained the elementary school teachers in the cooperative learning methods, the middle school teachers observed a profound difference in students coming from feeder schools where cooperative learning was taking place. The students were more polite, had a more positive attitude toward school, and were more oriented toward achievement. They were, simply put, better students. And then, a few years later, the high school teachers saw the difference and so they wanted training. The students were moving up and bringing the message with them!

Students Are Different. Today's high school students little resemble the students of my generation. I have talked with many older teachers and they confirm: Today's students are *different*. They report that they cannot get the same positive reaction from students today when they use the same teaching strategies. To engage students today, they have to use far more active and interactive instructional strategies.

When I attended high school, we looked up to our teachers. We wanted to please them, and learn from them. What a teacher said was important. There was respect for the teacher, school, and learning. Our teachers and classes were interesting. In fact, class was the most interesting thing in our world. Today all of that has changed. Fast-moving violent films, television, music videos, video games, and the Internet bombard today's high school students. The teacher and class are no longer the most interesting sources of stimulation. Whereas a lecture was an engaging source of stimulation for my generation, the same lecture is boring for today's youth — media has upped the ante!

How does that help explain the increased demand for cooperative learning at the high school level? Brain science reveals the brain is more engaged during social interaction than any other time.[5] When we institute cooperative learning, students immediately become engaged.

Peer interaction can compete with the acquired need for fast-moving stimulation; a lecture cannot. Students come to school not to listen to a teacher, but to interact with their peers. Cooperative learning allows students to do what they most want to do. Research reveals that students not only learn more when we use cooperative learning, but they also like school, class, and content more. Cooperative learning is the instructional methodology of choice for today's students.

Employability Skills.

Consciously and unconsciously, our educational system is preparation for participation in the workforce. Traditional methods in which students were told what to do and expected to do it paralleled the traditional workplace in which a boss told the employee what to do and the employee was expected to do it. Today's workplace is different. High technology has led to specialization which has led simultaneously to independence and interdependence. Employees with their very specialized skills are given tasks, but are expected to use creativity and initiative in fulfilling them. The boss cannot possibly know all the specialized skills of today's employees; the employees have to make decisions on their own. At the same time, they have to work with one another. No one person can design and make a state-of-the-art computer. Today's workplace is dominated by teamwork. Teams work on components, coordinating their efforts with other teams. Over 70% of today's employees work in teams as part of their regular job, and the number is increasing.[6] Today's teachers and administrators realize that the traditional approach to structuring a class (teacher

as boss) will not prepare students to make decisions, work creatively, and acquire teamwork skills. Cooperative learning is becoming popular at the high school level partly because it prepares students for the kind of world they will enter.

Block Scheduling.

More than anything else, increased demand for cooperative learning training at the high school level resulted from one factor: Block Scheduling. When block scheduling was instituted, high school teachers in all content areas became intensely aware that they needed to retool their instructional methodology. They could get away with an hour lecture, but neither the students nor the teachers could make it through the entire block with exclusive use of the traditional chalk and talk approach. With block scheduling, demand for secondary Cooperative Learning resources and trainings dramatically increased. Literally, cooperative learning had grown up.

Resources.

The increased demand for secondary resources and trainings in cooperative learning is supported also by more responsive publications and workshops. *Cooperative Learning & Science* is another milestone along that path. With their *Cooperative Learning & Science*, Michael, Angela, and Janina are doing for high school science teachers exactly what Dina Kusnir did for high school math teachers. They show how selected cooperative learning structures can be used across the curriculum to generate powerful, engaging lessons with any content. In the last few years, we have begun providing subject-specific workshops for secondary teachers. Rather than interacting with a primary teacher to discuss how to use a structure, secondary teachers process cooperative learning methods by interacting with fellow secondary teachers in their own content specialty.

Structures. Secondary teachers are learning the power of structures. Structures are an easy and effective approach to cooperative learning. Let's take a closer look at the many advantages of Kagan Structures.

Kagan Structures

Older models of cooperative learning were lesson-based. That is, the model demanded that teachers design and implement complex cooperative learning lessons. The message with the lesson-based approach: Stop teaching the way you have been teaching, we will show you a better way. It is difficult, if not impossible, to spend each night planning brand new lessons while maintaining content integrity.

In contrast to the lesson-based approach, the structure-based approach to cooperative learning provides a very different message: Keep teaching what you have always taught; keep your existing lessons. Structures will allow you to make those lessons more engaging, efficient, and successful. Structures demand little or no special planning time and do not demand a radical transformation of existing lessons. Structures are simple instructional strategies that make a world of difference. For those of you new to the concept of structures, let me provide an example.

For purposes of comparison, let's contrast RallyRobin with the traditional way we have students respond to questions in our classroom. RallyRobin is one of the simplest of all the Kagan

Structures — it can be used with no preparation and no change in content, at almost any point in a lesson. In a RallyRobin, students in pairs take turns speaking, usually naming things from a list, recalling or generating ideas. In a science class, RallyRobin may be used to have students take turns generating possible alternative explanations for a phenomenon.

For our comparison, let's look into the classrooms of two different teachers who want their students to review the inert elements:

- **Traditional class:** The teacher says, *"Without looking at the periodic table, who in the class can name an inert element?"* Students then raise their hands to be called on.
- **Kagan Structures:** The teacher uses the structure RallyRobin. He says, *"Turn to your partner and do a RallyRobin naming inert elements without looking at the periodic table."* Each student then takes a turn with his/her partner, each naming an element and then waiting for his/her partner to name the next one.

These two teachers have structured the interaction in their classroom differently — they are using different structures.

What are the benefits of using the cooperative structure RallyRobin rather than the traditional structure? The list is long. To name a few:

- Every student in the class generates several answers, as opposed to a selected few students generating one answer each

- All students are engaged so none tune out or get off task
- Half the class is answering at any one moment as opposed to only one student in the class
- The teacher can authentically assess students' knowledge by listening in to a randomly selected group, instead of just hearing from the high achievers
- Students like the variety; they say the structures are fun
- Students with answers become a resource rather than being put down as "know it alls" or "brown nosers"
- Students feel mutually supportive, not in competition with one another for teacher approval
- Test scores go up
- Students acquire teamwork skills and attitudes

This last point, that students learn to work in teams, is particularly important for science instruction. The day of the mythical "lone scientist" has come and gone. As science has become more sophisticated and complex, scientific inquiry is conducted increasingly by interdependent teams. The sole authorship of science papers was first replaced by co- and multiple authorships. Today, numerous interdependent teams, often in different labs, coordinate efforts and conduct science. As science continues to build on the complex methodologies and findings that are being established, interdependence among scientists will become even more the norm and teamwork skills will be prerequisite for full participation in the scientific community.

The structures you find in *Cooperative Learning & Science* are carefully selected to improve science instruction. They represent a range of types of structures.

Pairs Check is used following an introduction of a new skill; it is guided practice to master the skill. The skill can be anything from solving a type of equation to adjusting the flame on a Bunsen burner. The advantage of Pairs Check is that students get immediate supportive feedback and coaching; they do not have to wait until after you grade papers. An added advantage for teachers, of course, is that Pairs Check eliminates a great deal of unnecessary grading of worksheets.

Find Someone Who is active practice in consulting. Instead of treating a text as the ultimate or sole source, students find consultants in the class to help them find answers. An added benefit of Find Someone Who is that it allows students to get up from their desks and move around the room; a welcome break, especially if you are teaching on the block.

Mix-N-Match also energizes the class through movement. It is geared to the type of content that typically comprises the matching part of an exam. *Cooperative Learning & Science* provides ready-made blackline masters for Mix-N-Match. (Hint: Copy the cards onto colored cardstock and laminate them before cutting them to make an enduring set that can be used year after year.)

Corners allows students to express their preferences and to know and appreciate their classmates. In a secondary science class, the most powerful form of Corners is to have each member of the team go to a different corner of the room, gaining expertise from classmates that he/she can share after returning to teammates. Corners leads to content mastery, but in the process provides a great boost to self-esteem and peer acceptance because each teammate makes a unique, valuable contribution.

Give One–Get One also allows students to become experts, then share their expertise with others. An answer I "Get" from a classmate becomes an answer I "Give" to another classmate, and to my teammates at the end of the activity. In the process, I learn more. As we teach, we learn.

Word Webs are a wonderful exercise in the type of relational thinking core to so much of science. Important fields of science aim at understanding non-linear, mutually interactive webs of relationships. Traditional outlines cannot easily depict those relationships. How do I show in an outline a link between IIA1 and IIIC2? In a Word Web, the relationship is expressed with a simple arrow.

Agree-Disagree Line-Ups is a structure to use when discussing science related ethics. Science education today cannot escape value issues. We can make a human from an egg of an unborn fetus. But should we? We can tell if someone is prejudiced (whether he/she knows it or not) by doing a brain scan of the amygdala as he/she is shown pictures of faces of people of different races. But should we? Should brain scans that reveal amount of impulsivity be considered in determining early parole for prisoners who have committed violent crimes? Today's students will shape the future of our society as they vote on value issues like these. It is not our job as science educators to teach values, but it is our job to have students reflect on and think more deeply about the value issues inherent in our content. The perfect structure for this is Agree-Disagree Line-Ups. As students come to listen to, understand, and respect points of view different from their own, they become more thoughtful and articulate.

Avoiding Two Sins

There are two ways to go wrong as we have students work together to do science: Group Work and Group Grades. It not hard to find teachers who report, *"I tried cooperative learning and it did not work!"* What they don't realize is that they violated basic principles of cooperative learning, probably by doing group work or by using group grades. The authors of *Cooperative Learning & Science* gracefully side-step these traps.

Group Work is unstructured interaction. A teacher gives students a problem or a task and tells them to work together. The results are predictable and terrible. The high achiever, not wanting for the group to do poorly, takes over. Resentments build on both sides: The high achiever thinks, *"I had to do it all;"* the low achiever feels, *"I was not included."* Unstructured work in groups is wishful thinking. We hope the students will all participate and learn, but we have not taken responsibility for creating those outcomes. Structures are carefully designed to avoid the pitfalls of group work; they structure interaction to include the PIES principles: Positive Interdependence, Indivdiual Accountability, Equal Participation, and Simultaneous Interaction.[7] Each teammate participates about equally and is accountable for his/her contribution. The structures in *Cooperative Learning & Science* are carefully designed to include the PIES principles and avoid the trap of group work.

Group Grades also violate basic principles of cooperative learning and produce lamentable outcomes. The teacher gives a project to a group and then gives the project a grade. Each person on the team gets that grade for the project. Predictably, group grades produce free riders. Johnny does no work at all on the project, but gets a good grade because his teammates completed a first-rate project. Or, Johnny does a great job on the project, but gets a lower grade because Susie did a poor job on her part. Group grades are unfair and create a backlash against cooperative learning.[8] Cooperative learning is designed to promote learning; if we want to assess the effects of our instruction, there is no alternative to assessing the effects on individual learners. *Cooperative Learning & Science* provides structures for learning; it avoids the trap of group grades.

An Appreciation

Michael Michels, Angela Manzi, and Janina Mele have made an important contribution to the process of releasing the power of cooperative learning in high school classrooms. With *Cooperative Learning & Science*, any high school science teacher will find ready-made, proven activities. Be careful, though. The book should come with a warning label: *Caution Advised. Use of the Enclosed Activities Is Likely to Lead to an Addiction!* All it will take is trying a few of these activities in your own classroom and observing the reaction and performance of students, and you will get hooked. The wonderful thing, though, is that once you have mastered a structure, you will find it easy to generate your own activities for any content you teach. *Cooperative Learning & Science* is a springboard to a new way of teaching. Try it. You may well get hooked.

Good luck,

Spencer Kagan
June 14, 2003

References

[1] Johnson, D.W., Maruyama, G., Johnson, R. Nelson, D. & Skon, L. *Effects of cooperative, competitive and individualistic goal structures on achievement: a meta-analysis.* Psychological Bulletin, 1981, 89, 47–62.

[2] Morton, T. Cooperative Learning & Social Studies. San Clemente, CA: Kagan Publishing, 1998.

[3] Kushnir, D. Cooperative Learning & Mathematics: High School Activities. San Clemente, CA: Kagan Publishing, 2001.

[4] Bride, B. Cooperative Learning & High School Geometry. San Clemente, CA: Kagan Publishing, 2002.

[5] Carter, R. Mapping the Mind. Berkeley, CA: University of California Press, 1998.

[6] Filipczak, B. Industry Report. *What do workplace teams do?* Training Magazine, 1994, 31(10), 59–65.

[7] Kagan, S. Cooperative Learning. San Clemente, CA: Kagan Publishing, 1993.

[8] Kagan, S. *Group grades miss the mark.* Educational Leadership, 1995, 52(8), 68–71.

Introduction

**Dedicated to
Dan Kuzma,
our colleague, our friend, our inspiration.**

The high school science classroom is an ideal setting for cooperative learning. The interaction of students during a laboratory exercise and the inquisitive nature of the subject matter both provide opportunities for student interaction as no other discipline does. The question that arises is why aren't more high school science teachers using cooperative learning? There are many answers that come to mind, *"I don't have time to redo my lessons." "I don't know how to arrange my groups." "I have a hard time getting my students to work together well." "The cooperative classroom seems so disorganized." "I don't know what structure to use."* If you've had any of these thoughts, then you will find this book helpful!

The Cooperative Learning Experiment: Our Personal Stories

Before we get into an introduction of Kagan Structures and what's in this book, let's begin by sharing our personal experiences with cooperative learning and how we came together to write this book.

Janina Mele

Twelve years ago I had the fortune of attending an afternoon workshop that featured Spencer Kagan. To be honest, I had never heard of Spencer Kagan, but that afternoon meeting changed my life both professionally and personally. Forty-five minutes of an overview of Cooperative Learning and I was captivated. I was at that point a seasoned teacher with 25 years of experience. I needed something new in my repertoire to keep me interested and interesting. This was it. Over the next two years, our school provided us with the opportunity to have extensive training with Spencer and Laurie Kagan, and to become proficient in Cooperative Learning. This set me on a twelve-year path of creativity and learning I had never anticipated.

As a high school chemistry teacher, I thought I had an ideal setting. My students were already in a cooperative environment; I just needed to perfect it. Within a very short period of time, with good team construction, I found the social skills and connectedness of my students rising sharply. Students, who previously balked at working together, were now active and productive members of a team. I found myself becoming more linked to my students. We were building a new community in my room. Student self-esteem began to rise and hidden strengths began to surface. Students that I had two years before as a very traditional teacher, who would never raise their hands, were now walking to the board to share their team responses with confidence. When I surveyed my classes about the process of instruction for the year, one common statement was, "This is the only class I have gotten to know and work with everyone. It was great!"

In that very first year as a Cooperative Learning teacher, and thereafter, I noticed a sharp increase in scholastic achievement. As I recorded my grades for the second marking period, I seemed to be writing A far too many times. Upon closer examination, I discovered some startling facts: In one class, 17 out of 23 students earned an A, my class averages rose approximately 7% over my last year as a traditional teacher (at that point my testing was still traditional), and my classified students were performing one to two grade levels higher. Something wonderful was happening!!

Many of the structures I used were for skill acquisition. I will never forget the first Pairs Check I used in class. I stood in the back of the room and could not believe my eyes. All 26 students were working on Chemistry. This was surely a first! Using structures like this enabled me to move around the room to offer help, and made my role as a facilitator immensely more important. I also found that the student tutoring was very valuable to the learning process that was taking place. Interestingly enough, I discovered my students were no longer asking about the GRADE. They were happy to take home a corrected sheet along with a clear understanding of the process. All in all, a quantum leap!

Over the next 10 years, I compiled a massive library of Cooperative Learning activities, worksheets, and graphic organizers. Many of them appear in this book. They are, indeed, tried and true!

Angela Manzi

One year into my teaching career, I was looking for something to enliven my teaching strategies. Things just weren't working. Two colleagues were running a graduate course on Kagan's Cooperative Learning Structures. I registered, not knowing what I was about to learn. I left the workshop energized and excited, ready to try Kagan's Structures in my classroom. I was fortunate to have my colleagues there so I could share ideas with them as we continued to learn about and use cooperative learning. The results were amazing. Not only did I feel better about teaching, but my students were more responsive. Students at all ability levels were doing better in class. I was able to reach more difficult students in ways that had never seemed possible before learning about cooperative learning structures. I could actually see their behavior, self-esteem, and academic achievement improving in my classroom. The teambuilding and classbuilding activities went a long way toward making science laboratory work a more pleasurable and meaningful experience for my students. The bonding process among teammates completely revitalized the atmosphere in the classroom. I can't believe teaching strategies like cooperative learning were not part of my teacher education program. A few years later, I attended another Kagan workshop on cooperative learning with Michael and Jan. It was at this workshop that the three of us discussed this book with Dr. Spencer Kagan. The activities are real. They have been used in our classrooms — with success! We hope you enjoy using the activities in this book, and hope that they will provide you with ideas for creating cooperative learning activities of your own.

Michael Michels

As a first year teacher, I was brought in a few days earlier than the rest of the teachers for orientation. On that first day, I was greeted into my district by Dan Kuzma and Janina Mele, two teachers in the district that were helping with orientation, making the new teachers feel comfortable, and showing us the ropes of the school and the profession. Dan and Jan immediately utilized Kagan Structures in their orientation activities with us. We were immersed in a setting where we each communicated with one another and all participated equally. By the time the first day was over, I had met everyone in the room, knew much about them, and felt very comfortable with my new career. The structures they used were not only ice-breakers, they were classbuilding structures that we could use with our own students with the same results. I took a lot with me that day about this "new" way to engage an audience.

When I spoke with Dan later in the year about what he had shown me, he encouraged me to attend a workshop presented by Spencer and Laurie Kagan. I attended with Dan, Jan, and Angela, and my eyes were opened to this remarkable approach of engaging students. At this workshop, we discussed this book with Spencer. I felt honored since I was relatively new to this approach. That was four years ago. Since then, I have learned many Kagan Structures and have used them in all of my classes. I have seen amazing results with just about every Kagan Structure.

My high school science students — from freshman to seniors, from basic level to honors — have all grown remarkably from the use of Kagan Structures. I have seen a tremendous increase in participation. Students develop their interpersonal skills as they interact with classmates. There is a sense of belongingness and unity in the room. My students also have achieved better grades since I began using structures. I attribute it primarily to the increase in participation and communication among fellow students.

Lastly is a point about high school science specifically. Many times we are asked to teach schedules of more than the traditional 40 minute period. Many of us have lab periods (80 minutes), or Block Scheduling. Kagan's approach is an amazing asset to the science teacher during these large blocks of time. It is my hope that fellow teachers see the value in the ideas presented in this book. The structures, with the blacklines and ideas we provide, will energize you and your students and motivate them to achieve, just as they continue to do for me.

Kagan Structures

This book is based on a particular approach to cooperative learning, called Kagan Structures. The Kagan Structures model was developed by Dr. Spencer Kagan and his colleagues. Kagan Structures is a comprehensive approach to cooperative learning involving student teams, creating the will for students to cooperate, empowering students with the skills to work together, managing the cooperative classroom, developing social skills, and implementing basic principles through structures.

This book focuses on one aspect of the Kagan model — the structures. The Kagan Structures are instructional strategies. The intent of this book is to illustrate how to use Kagan Structures to more efficiently deliver high school science content. We do not address other cooperative learning issues, such as how to form teams, how long teams are to last, how to set up your classroom, how to manage your teams, and many other questions that arise when using cooperative learning. For these issues, we highly recommend Dr. Kagan's book, *Cooperative Learning*. It is the most comprehensive guide to cooperative learning.

What we offer in this book is a handful of powerful structures that transform delivery of any high school science curriculum. There are a number of distinct advantages of the Kagan Structures:

Structures Are Easy To Learn

Kagan Structures are simple. They are not complicated instructional strategies; they do not require a big time investment to learn. We have tried in this book to make the structures even easier by presenting the structures step-by-step and offering sample student instructions to help you introduce the structures to your students. You will find the techniques herein to be quite easy to pick up and integrate into your teaching repertoire.

Structures Are Easy To Implement

Most Kagan Structures require very little preparation. Once you learn a structure, it is easy to integrate the structure into your daily lessons. Our recommendation is that you select one structure. Get familiar with that structure. Try it with different content in different parts of your lesson. Let your students get comfortable with the new structure. When you've mastered your first structure, move on to learning the next one. Before long, you will have a new set of teaching tools. You'll look at your content differently; you'll have a range of options to make the content more interesting and fun to deliver and more engaging for your students.

Structures Make Learning Fun

Interacting over the content is fun. The structures in this book involve cooperative interaction with others in the class. Working together to learn together is more fun than working alone. This is especially true for high school students who cherish the opportunity to interact. Rather than bucking students' needs to be social, we channel that energy into science learning. Students' needs are being met while they are exploring the science curriculum. When learning becomes fun, it is more effective.

Structures Promote Science Learning

Beyond being just fun, the structures involve hands-on interaction with science content. With the structures in this book, students get the opportunity to get out of their seats, ask questions of teammates and classmates, display their knowledge, work together on team tasks, tutor one another, discuss issues, and create visual representations of their understanding of the content. Students develop teamwork skills and science process skills.

In addition, interacting over the science curriculum, students learn much more. Surely engaging teacher-directed instruction can promote learning. However, teacher input is more effective when punctuated with opportunities to interact over the content. Kagan Structures are a terrific way to break up direct instruction, especially when using Block Scheduling. Introduce one of these structures into your lesson, and watch enthusiasm over the content escalate! As soon as we put the learning in students' hands, something magical happens. That's the goal of Kagan Structures and this book — to unleash excitement over the content, making learning more successful.

Structures Have Powerful Built-In Principles

Cooperative learning is one of the most extensively researched innovations of all time. Research has consistently found that cooperative learning, when implemented successfully, is a successful tool for improving academic performance.

Some teachers report problems with cooperative learning. In reality, most are not doing true cooperative learning, but instead are using some form of group work. Group activities that are not carefully structured often reflect the input of only one or two students. True cooperative learning is orchestrated so students are on the same side, each accountable for his/her own learning, actively participating about equally.

The structures in this book implement the basic principles of cooperative learning using easy instructional strategies. Kagan identifies four basic principles: 1) Positive Interdependence, 2) Individual Accountability, 3) Equal Participation, 4) Simultaneous Interaction. The four basic principles are symbolized by the acronym, PIES. Below is a brief description of the PIES principles and the critical question(s) for ensuring each principle is in place:

POSITIVE INTERDEPENDENCE
Students are working together. They are on the same side, not isolated or in competition with other students in the classroom.
Critical Questions: *Is a gain for one a gain for all? Is help needed?*

INDIVIDUAL ACCOUNTABILITY
Each student is accountable for his/her own learning and displaying what he/she has learned. Individual accountability ensures that all students are learning and participating, not a select few in each team.
Critical Question: *Is a public performance required by all students in the group?*

EQUAL PARTICIPATION
Without equal participation, students may be satisfied to let teammates do the work, in which case learning seldom occurs. Active participation by each student is essential for each to student to learn.
Critical Question: *How equal is the participation?*

SIMULTANEOUS INTERACTION
Simultaneous interaction deals with the quantity of student overt participation. In addition to being about equal, there should be a lot of active participation. With this principle, we strive for an abundance of overt participation occurring in each team.
Critical Question: *How many students are overtly involved at one time?*

The inclusion of these principles during cooperative learning is what distinguishes cooperative learning from group work. True cooperative learning leads to fewer problems and increased productivity and achievement. The wonderful thing about the Kagan Structures in this book is that they have the PIES principles built in. You don't have to worry about instituting these somewhat abstract learning principles to create effective cooperative learning activities for your students; you simply select a structure. When you use a Kagan Structure, you can feel confident that you're putting effective learning principles to work in your classroom.

Structures Are Flexible
As you will see throughout this book, structures are acrobats! Each structure is presented with a range of activity ideas and blacklines across the major science content areas. A single structure can be used with a wide variety of science content. A single activity is used successfully only once. When you learn one new structure, you are equipped to create many, new activities.

There are over 150 Kagan Structures. Some structures are designed to encourage classbuilding and teambuilding. Others are used to enhance content mastery or develop higher-level thinking. Still others are used to share information and develop better communication skills. The six structures chosen for this book are a small sampling of possible structures to enliven your science classroom.

In This Book
The six Kagan Structures featured in this book are: 1) Find Someone Who, 2) Pairs Check, 3) Corners, 4) Mix-N-Match, 5) Word

Webbing, and 6) Give One–Get One. For each structure, there is a structure page, contents page, activity ideas, and blacklines across the major science areas.

Structure Page

The structure page outlines the structure step-by-step and provides sample instructions to give to the students. This structure page is your guide for using the structure.

Structure Contents Page

After the presentation of each structure, there are activity ideas and blackline masters across four major science disciplines — Biology, Chemistry, Earth Science, and Physical Science. Each structure also includes activities and/or blacklines for general science classes or generic forms that can be used for different science classes. The content pages will steer you in the right direction for your subject specialty.

Activity Ideas

The activity ideas for each structure are designed to prime the pump. They are provided to help you generate ideas to use the structure in your classroom. You will find some activity ideas you will be able to use right away; others will spark ideas that you can turn into activities.

Blackline Masters

The blackline masters in this book are reproducible activities you can use with your class. Depending on the structure, some are for individuals, others for pairs, and others for the team. You're sure to find lots of blacklines you'll be able to use right away.

Content Charts

In the beginning of the book, there is a contents page for each major science content area featured in this book. These content pages will be helpful for those of you who teach just one science class and are looking for ideas specific to your class.

It is also designed as an easy reference to find activities and blacklines that you may be searching for at a later date.

The structures in this book barely touch the surface of cooperative learning, but they should provide you with a launch pad to success. They have been field-tested for many years and have proven to be very successful in high school science. Feel free to use them as designed, or modify them to meet your own needs. That's the beauty of cooperative learning! Have fun!

Michael P. Michels
Biology/Physical Science Teacher

Angela L. Manzi
Biology/Chemistry Teacher

Janina A. Mele
Retired Chemistry Teacher,
Cooperative Learning Graduate Trainer

Indian Hills High School
Oakland, New Jersey

Acknowledgements

We are especially grateful to Spencer and Miguel Kagan for setting us on the best path of presentation. In addition, thanks to Spencer for writing the Foreword to this book and to Miguel for his role as project manager and content editor. We are also indebted to the people who play such an important role behind the scenes. Miles Richey designed and executed the attractive page layout and was responsible for collecting and creating the many illustrations that fill this book. Celso Rodriguez illustrated the cover. Alex Core designed the cover and colored the cover. Kathy Tomlinson copyedited the final draft of the book. Thank you to everyone who made this book possible.

Science
Structures

BIOLOGY
BIOLOGY

PHYSICAL SCIENCE

Find Someone Who...

ENERAL SCIENCE

CHEMISTRY

EARTH SCIENCE

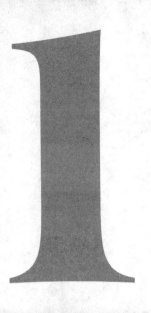

Find Someone Who

Students mix about the room
finding others who help them learn content
or skills, or who have certain characteristics.

1 Students mix in the class, keeping a hand raised until they find a new partner who is not a teammate.

2 In pairs, Partner A asks a question from the worksheet; Partner B responds. Partner A records the answer on his or her own worksheet.

3 Partner B checks and initials the answer.

4 Partner B asks a question; Partner A responds. Partner B records the answer on his or her own worksheet.

5 Partner A checks and initials the answer.

6 Partners shake hands, part, and raise a hand again as they search for a new partner.

7 Students repeat steps 1-6 until their worksheets are complete.

8 When their worksheets are completed, students sit down; seated students can be approached by others as a resource.

9 In teams, students compare answers; if there is disagreement or uncertainty, they raise four hands to ask a team question.

Student Instructions:
Stand up with your worksheet and a pen. Raise your hand until you find a partner. Ask your partner one question from your worksheet. If your partner knows the answer, write the answer on your worksheet and have your partner sign or initial that it is correct. If your partner doesn't know the answer and you do, tell your partner, but don't fill in your answer. Switch roles and let your partner ask you a question. Thank your partner, raise your hand and find a new partner.

Find Someone Who...
Activities & Blacklines

Biology

A. Activity Ideas

B. Blackline Masters

Chemistry

A. Activity Ideas

B. Blackline Masters

Earth Science

A. Activity Ideas

B. Blackline Masters

Physical Science

A. Activity Ideas

B. Blackline Masters

General Science

A. Blackline Masters

1. Body Systems

Objective: Students will share information with classmates while reviewing human body systems.

Find Someone Who...	Signature
1. can name the system responsible for excretion of waste.	
2. can name the system that contains the right atrium.	

2. Organs

Objective: Students will share information with classmates while reviewing organ parts and functions.

Find Someone Who...	Signature
1. can name the organ of the digestive system that mechanically breaks down food.	
2. can name the organ responsible for gas exchange.	

3. Mitosis

Objective: Students will share information with classmates while reviewing stages of mitosis and the cell cycle.

Find Someone Who...	Signature
1. can draw a cell in the anaphase stage.	
2. can name the stage where the cleavage furrow is forming.	

4. Photosynthesis

Objective: Students will share information with classmates while reviewing the reactions and purpose of photosynthesis.

Find Someone Who...	Signature
1. can tell what happens to water in the light reactions.	
2. can write the formula for glucose.	

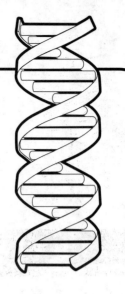

DNA Hunt...

Instructions: Find someone who can complete a task or knows the answer to one of these questions and have him/her explain it to you. After sharing the information, have that person initial your paper. Be prepared to explain that person's answer. Continue with another student until the worksheet is completed.

1. _____ has experienced a spiral staircase or slide.

2. _____ is wearing clothing with a zipper.

3. _____ has jeans on.

4. _____ knows triplets.

5. _____ knows someone who uses blueprints.

6. _____ can name a substance that bonds things together.

7. _____ can name the four bases found in DNA and RNA.

8. _____ can describe a double helix formation using his/her hands.

9. _____ can take the 1st, 5th, and 20th letters of the alphabet and make three different words with them.

Biomes of the World

Instructions: Find someone who can do what each statement below requests. Have him/her do what it says about the biome and place it in the answer column; then put his/her initials by the corresponding line. Continue until your sheet is complete. Each person may only sign your sheet once.

Find Someone Who...

	Signature	Answer
1. knows what biome we live in.		
2. can name one species in the temperate deciduous forest.		
3. has been to a tropical rain forest.		
4. can name two zones of the marine biome.		
5. can name a state that is within the coniferous forest.		
6. knows the name of a desert in the United States.		
7. can tell how much precipitation the tundra receives each year.		
8. is going to vacation in a biome other than our own this year.		
9. can explain what permafrost is.		
10. knows one biome in Australia.		
11. can name three examples of bodies of water that are considered freshwater zones.		

1. Symbol Recognition

Objective: Students will share information with classmates while reviewing symbols from the Periodic Table of the Elements.

Find Someone Who...	Signature
1. can name the symbol Sn.	
2. can write the symbol for tungsten.	

2. Formula Recognition

Objective: Students will share information with classmates while reviewing chemical nomenclature.

Find Someone Who...	Signature
1. can name the compound Fe (II) $(OH)_2$.	
2. can write the formula for ammonium sulfate.	

3. Periodic Table Recognition

Objective: Students will share information with classmates while reviewing symbols and periodicity from the Periodic Table of the Elements.

Find Someone Who...	Signature
1. can name one element from the halogen Family.	
2. can name one alkali metal that is more reactive than Na.	

4. Chemical Properties Recognition

Objective: Students will share information with classmates while reviewing chemical properties.

Find Someone Who...	Signature
1. can name the lightest gas.	
2. can name one element that is chemically inert.	

5. Chemical Reactions Recognition

Objective: Students will share information with classmates while reviewing chemical properties.

Find Someone Who...	Signature
1. can describe how an ionic bond forms.	
2. can draw the hydrogen bonds found in water.	

Kagan Publishing • 1 (800) 933-2667
www.KaganOnline.com

Chemical Hunt

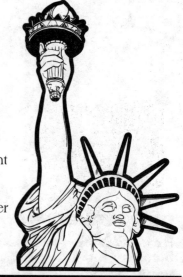

Instructions: Read the statements below. Move around the classroom and find another person. Ask him/her to do what one statement requests. The person must be able to identify the element or compound by symbol in order to sign your paper. Thank the person and find a new partner to repeat the process. Continue until all answer boxes are completed. Each person may only sign once.

Find Someone Who...

	Signature	Answer
1. is wearing a silver earring.		
2. knows the gas dissolved in soda.		
3. can identify the gas in a blimp.		
4. knows the silver liquid metal in a thermometer.		
5. knows the element that makes strong bones.		
6. can name the main fuel in the sun.		
7. can name the white substance you put on french fries.		
8. knows the element found in Fort Knox.		
9. can identify the compound that makes the Statue of Liberty blue-green.		
10. knows the chemical symbol for rust.		

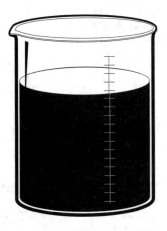

Who Knows Their Acids and Bases?

Instructions: Find someone who can do what each statement below requests. Have him/her fill in the answer column before signing your sheet. Continue until your sheet is complete. Each person may only sign your sheet once.

Find Someone Who...

	Signature	Answer
1. knows the pH of water.		
2. can identify the H_3O^{+1} ion.		
3. can write the formula for sulfuric acid.		
4. can describe titration.		
5. can name two products of neutralization.		
6. can write the formula for sodium hydroxide.		
7. can name the OH^{-1} ion.		
8. can tell what color blue litmus paper turns in an acid.		
9. can identify one food that is an acid.		
10. used a base today and for what.		

1. Natural Disaster Recognition

Objective: Students will share information with classmates while reviewing types of natural disasters.

Find Someone Who...	Signature
1. can describe the motion of air molecules in a tornado.	
2. can list one distinguishing characteristic between a tornado and a hurricane.	

2. Mineral Recognition

Objective: Students will share information with classmates while reviewing minerals.

Find Someone Who...	Signature
1. can describe how the numbers differ in Moh's Scale of Hardness.	
2. can name the softest mineral.	

3. Weather Terms Recognition

Objective: Students will share information with classmates while reviewing types of weather.

Find Someone Who...	Signature
1. can describe the characteristics of a jet stream.	
2. can name two effects of El Niño.	

4. Topographic Terms Recognition

Objective: Students will share information with classmates while reviewing topographic terms.

Find Someone Who...	Signature
1. can define plateau.	
2. can draw a picture of a peninsula.	

Wild Weather Worksheet

Instructions: Find someone who can do what each of the statements below requests. Have him/her do what it says and put his/her initials by the corresponding cloud. Continue until your sheet is complete. Each person may only sign your sheet once.

Find Someone Who...

can name one instrument used to measure wind speed _____

knows where a maritime tropical airmass originates

has experienced a hurricane

has experienced a sea breeze _____

knows the wind speed of an F4 tornado _____

can name the three stages of thunderstorm development _____

can give an everyday example of the Coriolis effect _____

can tell what pressure is associated with rainy weather _____

can draw a cirrus cloud _____

can draw a stratus cloud _____

Draw cloud here.

Draw cloud here.

A Cross Section of the Earth

Instructions: Find someone who can perform each task regarding the layers of the Earth. Have him/her do what it says and put his/her initials by the corresponding line. Continue until your sheet is complete. Each person may only sign your sheet once.

Find Someone Who...

		Initials	Answer
1.	can explain the difference between the inner and outer core.		
2.	knows what layer we live within.		
3.	has seen evidence of the Earth's inner heat.		
4.	can name the layers in order from outside to inside.		
5.	knows the depth of the crust.		
6.	can write the chemical symbol for the most abundant element of the mantle.		
7.	knows what layer is the farthest humans have mined to.		
8.	can draw a picture of the surface representing both continental and oceanic crust.		

1. Newton's Laws Recognition

Objective: Students will share information with classmates while reviewing Newton's Laws.

Find Someone Who...	Signature
1. can define momentum.	
2. can give one example of friction.	

2. Simple Machines Recognition

Objective: Students will share information with classmates while reviewing simple machines.

Find Someone Who...	Signature
1. can give one example of a first class lever.	
2. can describe how the mechanical advantage of a machine determines its efficiency.	

3. States of Matter Recognition

Objective: Students will share information with classmates while reviewing states of matter.

Find Someone Who...	Signature
1. can describe what happens at the molecular level when condensation takes place.	
2. can draw a picture of a gas sample.	

4. Types of Energy Recognition

Objective: Students will share information with classmates while reviewing types of energy.

Find Someone Who...	Signature
1. can describe what type of energy is commonly used in the home.	
2. can name an alternative energy source.	

Kagan Publishing • 1 (800) 933-2667
www.KaganOnline.com

Heat Energy Hunt

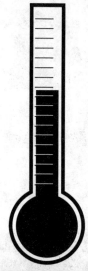

Instructions: Read the statements below. Move around the classroom and find another person. Ask him/her to do one of the tasks. The person must be able to do it correctly in order to sign your paper. Thank the person and find a new partner to repeat the process. Continue until all answer boxes are completed. Each person may only sign once.

Find Someone Who...

	Signature	Answer
1. knows the boiling point of water in degrees Fahrenheit.		
2. can convert 10 degrees Celsius to Kelvin.		
3. can name an example of a conductor of heat.		
4. knows the silver liquid metal in a thermometer.		
5. knows what absolute zero is in Celsius.		
6. can name a type of thermometer.		
7. can write the equation needed to convert Fahrenheit to Celsius.		
8. knows a source of radiation.		
9. can use his/her body to illustrate the kinetic energy from a hot to a cold substance.		
10. can name an insulator.		

Speedy Search

Instructions: Find someone who can complete the task in one of the following statements about motion. Have him/her do what it says and put his/her initials by the corresponding line. Continue until your sheet is complete. Each person can only sign your sheet once.

Find Someone Who...

	Signature	Answer
1. can tell what the acceleration of a car is while the cruise control is set at 55 mph.		
2. has been on an airplane and can describe what takeoff and landing have to do with acceleration and deceleration.		
3. can draw a graph of constant speed.		
4. can write the formula for acceleration.		
5. knows the difference between instantaneous and average speed.		
6. can tell if this statement is referring to speed or velocity: "A car is traveling southwest at 33 miles per hour."		
7. knows the SI units for velocity and acceleration.		
8. can write the formula for velocity.		
9. has accelerated at 9.8 m/s^2.		
10. can write the formula for momentum.		
11. can draw a graph of deceleration.		

Cooperative Learning Activities For High School Science

Kagan Publishing • 1 (800) 933-2667
www.KaganOnline.com

People Hunt

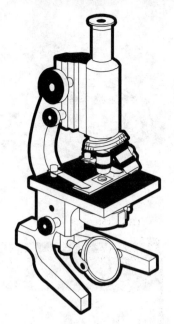

Instructions: Read the statements below, filling in the answers for yourself. Then move around the classroom and find another person. Read him/her one statement. If you find a match, sign each other's worksheet; if not, the person then asks you a question from his/her sheet looking for a match. Continue alternating questions until you find a match. Thank the person and find a new partner to repeat the process. Continue until all boxes are filled.

	Self	**Friend**
1. favorite after-school activity		
2. favorite subject		
3. favorite free-time activity		
4. favorite school lunch		
5. favorite school sport		
6. favorite season		
7. favorite place in school		
8. favorite class		
9. favorite teacher		
10. favorite school holiday		

Lab Bingo

Instructions: Find people who can complete the task or answer the question in each of the squares. Ask the question, have the person answer the question, and then have the person initial the square. When you have five signatures in a row, horizontally, vertically, or diagonally, call out "Lab Bingo!"

Find Someone Who...

can locate the eyewash	knows where the fire extinguisher is	knows where the safety goggles are	knows where the safety shut-off valve is	knows the proper way to mix acid and water
can demonstrate how to light a Bunsen burner	can demonstrate how to focus a microscope	can read the meniscus of a graduated cylinder and record its volume	knows where the fire blanket is	knows how to light a burner with a striker
can demonstrate how to mass an aobject on a triple beam balance	can demonstrate how to clean a test tube properly	**Free Space** Sign your name: _____	can demonstrate how to read a thermometer	knows what the expression "stop, drop, and roll" means
knows the proper lab attire	can demonstrate how to measure a sample block in cm	can convert 10°C to °F	knows where to place broken glass	can demonstrate the proper way to carry a balance
knows where the first aid kit is located	knows where the chemical waste container is	knows where the fire alarm is	can demonstrate how to waft an odor	can demonstrate the proper way to carry a microscope

Find Someone Who...

Instructions: Find someone who can answer one of the questions below. Have him/her write the answer and sign your sheet. Continue finding partners who can help you answer the questions until your sheet is complete. Each person can sign your sheet once.

Find Someone Who...	Signature	Answer
1.		
2.		
3.		
4.		
5.		
6.		
7.		
8.		
9.		
10.		

People Hunt

Instructions: Read the statements below, filling in the answers for yourself. Then move around the classroom and find another person and read him/her one statement. If you find a match, sign each other's worksheet; if not, the person then asks you a question from his/her sheet looking for a match. Continue alternating questions until you find a match. Thank the person and find a new partner to repeat the process. Continue until all boxes are filled.

	Self	Friend
1.		
2.		
3.		
4.		
5.		
6.		
7.		
8.		
9.		
10.		

Find Someone Who...
Bingo

Instructions: Find people who can complete the task or answer the question in each of the squares. Ask the question, have the person answer the question, and then have the person initial the square. When you have five signatures in a row, horizontally, vertically, or diagonally, call out "Lab Bingo!"

		Free Space		

PHYSICAL SCIENCE

BIOLOGY

Pairs Check

ENERAL SCIENCE

CHEMISTRY

EARTH SCIENCE

2 Pairs Check

In pairs, students take turns solving problems. After every two problems they check answers and celebrate with another pair.

1 In teams of four, shoulder partners are formed. Partner A in each pair does the first problem, talking out loud. Partner B watches and coaches. Partner B praises.

2 Reverse roles: Partner B does the second problem. Partner A watches, coaches, and praises.

3 Pairs check with their face partners after every two problems. Teammates coach and correct if needed.

4 The team celebrates after reaching agreement on the two problems.

5 Shoulder partners do more problems, continuing to check with their face partners after every two problems.

Student Instructions:
Pair up within your team. Partner A will answer the first problem while Partner B coaches. Partner B helps if necessary and praises Partner A when both agree. Partner B solves the next problem while Partner A coaches. Once both problems are finished, check with the other pair from your team. If you have different answers, determine which is correct. When you all agree, circle the check mark to the right and give a team handshake. Complete the problems in the same fashion.

Pairs Check
Activities & Blacklines

Biology

A. Activity Ideas

B. Blackline Masters

Chemistry

A. Activity Ideas

B. Blackline Masters

Earth Science

A. Activity Ideas

B. Blackline Masters

Physical Science

A. Activity Ideas

B. Blackline Masters

General Science

A. Activity Idea

B. Blackline Masters

1. Transcription/Translation

Objective: Students will work in pairs to solve and check one another's work for problems relating to protein synthesis.

ATCGCAT

Transcribe to mRNA

_____

AUG CCG UCA UAA

Translate to the amino acid sequence

_____

2. Reactions of Photosynthesis

Objective: Students will work in pairs to solve and check one another's work for problems relating to the reactions of photosynthesis.

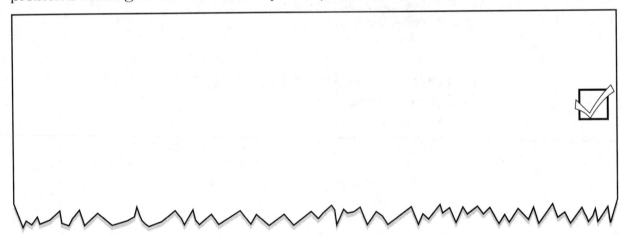

3. Terms of Cell Structure

Objective: Students will work in pairs to solve and check one another's work for problems relating to cell structures and organelles.

The protein factories are known as

_____

The lysosome is responsible for:

_____

4. Population Genetics

Objective: Students will work in pairs to solve and check one another's work for problems relating to Hardy-Weinberg & Genetics Probability.

The Hardy-Weinberg Equation is

_____

If 50% of the population is heterozygous for a trait, what is the frequency of the recessive allele?

_____

BIOLOGY BLACKline Pairs Check

Genetics

Instructions: On a separate sheet of paper, complete the Punnett Squares described.

Name: _____

Date: _____

Name: _____

Date: _____

1

Complete a Punnett Square for the following cross: GG x Gg

2

Complete a Punnett Square for the following cross: GG x gg

3

What would the phenotypic ratio be in a cross between a homozygous green pea plant and a heterozygous pea plant?

4

What would the genotypic ratio be in a cross between a homozygous short pea plant and a heterozygous tall pea plant?

5

Complete a Punnett Square with genotypic and phenotypic ratios for the following cross: a purebred smooth pea with a hybrid pea.

6

Complete a Punnett Square with genotypic and phenotypic ratios for the following cross: a purebred wrinkled pea with a hybrid pea.

7

Complete a Punnett square with phenotypic ratios for the following cross: two parents that are both hybrids for height and pea color.

8

Complete a Punnett Square with phenotypic ratios for the following cross: one parent that is hybrid for height and pea color, and one parent that is purebred recessive for both traits.

Sponge: Create and complete a genetic cross of your own.

Sponge: Create and complete a genetic cross of your own.

Innate or Learned?

Instructions: Write whether the behavior is "innate" or "learned" and write your reason for your answer.

Name: _____   Name: _____

Date: _____   Date: _____

1. Coughing	**2. Riding a Bicycle**
Type of Behavior:	Type of Behavior:
Reason:	Reason:
3. Tying Shoes	**4. Sneezing**
Type of Behavior:	Type of Behavior:
Reason:	Reason:
5. Sweating	**6. Shivering**
Type of Behavior:	Type of Behavior:
Reason:	Reason:
7. Having a Fever	**8. Eating with a Fork**
Type of Behavior:	Type of Behavior:
Reason:	Reason:
9. Biting Fingernails	**10. Feeling Pain**
Type of Behavior:	Type of Behavior:
Reason:	Reason:

Sponge: If your pair or team finishes early, then come up with at least five more examples of innate behavior and at least five more examples of learned behavior.

1. Balancing Equations

Objective: Students will work in pairs to solve and check one another's work for problems relating to balancing equations.

$$Na + H_2O \longrightarrow NaOH + H_2$$

$$Zn + HCl \longrightarrow ZnCl + H_2$$

2. Significant Digits/Math Operations

Objective: Students will work in pairs to solve and check one another's work for problems relating to significant digits and mathematical operations. (suggestion: make one worksheet for use in determining the number of significant digits and one sheet for calculations).

389003948

Determine the number of significant digits in the above number.

$$2.51 \times 3.7 =$$

Calculate the answer and express in the correct number of significant digits.

3. Naming Organic Molecules

Objective: Students will work in pairs to solve and check one another's work for problems relating to naming organic molecules (Make one sheet for naming compounds and another sheet for writing structural formulas).

C_2H_5OH

Name the compound.

Butanol

Write the structural formula.

4. Drawing Structural Formulas

Objective: Students will work in pairs to solve and check one another's work for problems relating to diagraming structural formulas of organic molecules.

C_2H_5OH

Draw the structural formula

C_5H_{10}

Draw the structural formula.

Stoichiometry

Instructions: Determine the number of moles for each problem.

Name: _____   Name: _____

Date: _____   Date: _____

1 How many moles are there in 66 g of Na?	**2** How many moles are there in 108 g of Al?
3 How many moles are there in 15 g of Cl_2?	**4** How many moles are there in 87 g of O ?
5 How many moles are there in 102.5 g of NaOH?	**6** How many moles are there in 54.6 g of H_2SO_4?
7 How many moles are there in 5.90 g of $MgBr_2$?	**8** How many moles are there in 47.6 g of $(NH_4)_2SO_4$?
Sponge:	Sponge:

Formulas

Instructions: Write the chemical formula for each word formula listed.

Name: _____   Name: _____

Date: _____   Date: _____

1 Sodium Chloride _____	**2** Magnesium Oxide _____
3 Aluminum Sulfide _____	**4** Potassium Oxide _____
5 Calcium Chloride _____	**6** Lithium Nitride _____
7 Lead(II) Oxide _____	**8** Iron(III) Fluoride _____
9 Copper(I) Oxide _____	**10** Zinc Sulfide _____
Sponge:	Sponge:

1. Astronomical Unit Conversions

Objective: Students will work in pairs to solve and check one another's work for problems relating to astronomical unit conversions.

How many miles are in .33 astronomical units?

Use the following orientation: Sun - Earth - Planet. If a planet is 4.3 astronomical units away from the Earth, how many miles is it away from the sun?

2. Half-Life Radioactive Problems

Objective: Students will work in pairs to solve and check one another's work for problems relating to half-life calculations.

If the half-life of an element is 8.2 years, how much of a 100-gram sample will be left after 16.4 years?

If a sample has a half-life of 25.5 years and has been decaying for 42.7 years, how many half-lives have gone by?

3. Phases of the Moon

Objective: Students will work in pairs to solve and check one another's work for problems relating to the phases of the moon.

Draw a half moon that is waxing.

What phase would the moon be in 7 days after it is new.

4. Scientific Notation and Math Operations

Objective: Students will work in pairs to solve and check one another's work for problems relating to exponential calculations.

What is the sum of 2.5 x 10 E7 and 33.6 x 10 E8?

What is the product of 7.5 x 10 E3 and 3.2 x 10 E4?

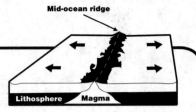

Mid-ocean ridge

Lithosphere   Magma

Plate Tectonics

Instructions: On a separate sheet of paper, write the answers to the following questions.

Name: _____   Name: _____

Date: _____   Date: _____

1 How are the Himalayas and the Alps alike?	**2** How is the Pacific Ocean different from the Atlantic Ocean?
3 Where is the sea floor growing?	**4** Why do trenches form near mountainous coasts?
5 Why are the eastern and western parts of Iceland moving farther apart?	**6** What happens when two plates collide?
7 What happens when two plates slide along each other?	**8** What is an example of an active volcano?
9 What type of volcano is Mt. St. Helens?	**10** What is an example of a volcanic island?
Sponge:	Sponge:

Chemical
Waste

Pollution

Instructions: Answer the pollution-related questions below.

Name: _____   Name: _____

Date: _____   Date: _____

1	2
What is the name of this type of pollution? NO_x _____	What is the name of this type of pollution? VOCs _____
3	**4**
What is the chemical formula for the pollutant called carbon monoxide? _____	What is the chemical formula for the pollutant called sulfur dioxide? _____
5	**6**
What is one pollutant that is caused naturally? _____	What is one pollutant that is man-made? _____
7	**8**
What is one product of combustion? _____	What is one reactant in combustion? _____
9	**10**
During what season of the year is carbon dioxide the highest in the atmosphere for the Earth? Why? (write answer on back)	What is the difference between the greenhouse effect and global warming? (write answer on back)
Sponge:	Sponge:

Cooperative Learning Activities For High School Science

Kagan Publishing • 1 (800) 933-2667
www.KaganOnline.com

1. Force Problems

Objective: Students will work in pairs to solve and check one another's work for problems relating to Newton's Laws.

If 2.5 newtons is applied to a mass of 6.77 grams, what is the acceleration?	If an object has a mass of 151 grams and is accelerating at a rate of 3.5 m/s/s, what is the force?

2. Work Equations

Objective: Students will work in pairs to solve and check one another's work for problems relating to work equations.

If a force of 5.6 newtons is applied to an object over a distance of 12 meters, how much work is accomplished?	If 75.7 joules of work is accomplished over a distance of 21 meters, what force is necessary?

3. Temperature Conversions

Objective: Students will work in pairs to solve and check one another's work for problems relating to temperature conversions.

Convert 25°C to °F.

Convert 34K to °C.

4. Circuits

Objective: Students will work in pairs to draw and check one another's work for problems relating to electric circuits.

Draw a series circuit containing the following: one open switch, three resistors, one light bulb and a voltmeter.

Draw a parallel circuit containing the following: two switches (one open and one closed), three light bulbs and one resistor.

PHYSICAL SCIENCE
BLACKline Pairs Check

Significant Digits

Instructions: Determine the number of significant digits for each problem below.

Name: _____   Name: _____

Date: _____   Date: _____

1	2
1004	527177
_____	_____

3	4
46.711	38.927
_____	_____

5	6
720000	61004100
_____	_____

7	8
0.0001492	0.0410100
_____	_____

9	10
Test your partner by making an example.	Test your partner by making an example.
_____	_____

Sponge: _____   Sponge: _____

Elements

Instructions: For each element, find the requested information, using your periodic table.

Name: _____   Name: _____

Date: _____   Date: _____

1

How many protons are in the element aluminum?

_____

2

How many protons are in the element zinc?

_____

3

How many electrons are in the element calcium?

_____

4

How many electrons are in the element lead?

_____

5

What is the atomic mass of the element silver (to three significant digits)?

_____

6

What is the atomic mass of the element fluorine (to three significant digits)?

_____

7

How many neutrons are in an atom of sodium?

_____

8

How many neutrons are in an atom of sulphur?

_____

9

Using the following information, how many neutrons are in this atom? Is it an isotope?

$^{27}_{13}\text{Al}$

(write answer on back)

10

Using the following information, how many neutrons are in this atom? Is it an isotope?

$^{14}_{6}\text{C}$

(write answer on back)

Sponge:

Sponge:

1. Right vs. Wrong Laboratory Procedures

Objective: Students will work in pairs to solve and check one another's work for topics relating to using and working with laboratory equipment.

Draw a picture of how to read a graduated cylinder.	Draw a picture of how to read a mercury barometer.

Observation/Inference

Instructions: Read each of the following scenarios and determine whether each is an observation or an inference.

Name: _____   Name: _____

Date: _____   Date: _____

1 I mass a test tube and find the contents to mass at 9.2 grams. Observation or Inference?	**2** A scientist watches a group of bees. More bees land on the yellow flowers than on the purple flowers. Observation or Inference?
3 A scientist sees bats being active at night, bats must be nocturnal. Observation or Inference?	**4** The yellow flowers, from above, must have more nectar than the purple flowers. Observation or Inference?
5 You shake a closed box and hear nothing, the box is empty. Observation or Inference?	**6** You shake a closed box and hear nothing, but you saw your friend place a feather in it before closing it. There is a feather inside the box. Observation or Inference?
7 You measure the sides of a cube to be 3cm. The volume of the cube is 27 cubic centimeters. Observation or Inference?	**8** Earlier in the lab, your partner massed a test tube to be 9.2 grams. The test tube that you need to mass feels a bit lighter, you concluded that the mass is 8.7 grams. Observation or Inference?
9 You are holding a peanut. Its shell is rough. Observation or Inference?	**10** You are holding a peanut. The peanuts inside the shell have a skin around them. Observation or Inference?
Sponge:	Sponge:

Pairs Check Worksheet

_____
(Topic)

Name: _____   Name: _____

Date: _____   Date: _____

1	2
3	4
5	6
7	8
9	10
Sponge:	Sponge:

Cooperative Learning Activities For High School Science

BIOLOGY
BIOLOGÍA

PHYSICAL SCIENCE

Corners

GENERAL SCIENCE

CHEMISTRY

EARTH SCIENCE

Corners

Students move to different corners of the room to interact with classmates on the same topic, and listen to ideas of classmates who selected different topics.

1 Teacher announces three or more corners.

2 Students think about, then write down their corner selection.

3 Students move to their corners.

4 Teacher provides content for interaction.

5 Pairs share using Timed Pair Share or RallyRobin.

6 Teacher calls on students from each corner to share with the class.

7 Students may be asked to paraphrase reasons of those from other corners using RallyRobin.

Teacher Note:
Corners is usually used for students to select a preference between alternatives. It is used here to further examine science content. Some possible ways to have students select their corners are:

- Which topic do you know most about?
- Which topic do you know least about?
- Which topic would you like to know more about?

The teacher may also assign each teammate a different corner.

Student Instructions:
Look at the pictures posted in the corners. In a minute you will be moving to one of these corners. Think about which corner you know the most about. Write your answer on a slip of paper. I will be giving you focus questions for you to discuss with students from your corner.

Corners
Activities & Blacklines

Biology

Chemistry

Earth Science

Physical Science

General Science

1. Macromolecules

Objective: Students will review the structure and function of macromolecules.

Corner 1: Carbohydrates
Corner 2: Lipids
Corner 3: Proteins
Corner 4: Nucleic Acids

See
Blackline
p.54

Focus Questions:
• What are the monomers?
• What are the functions?
• Where can I be found in the real world?
• Where can I be found in the body?
• What is my use in the human body?

2. Kingdoms of Life

Objective: Students will review the diversity and unity of the five kingdoms of life.

Corner 1: Animalia
Corner 2: Plantae
Corner 3: Fungi
Corner 4: Protista
Corner 5: Monera

Focus Questions:
• What are three characteristics that describe my kingdom?
• What is the structure of my typical cell? (Draw it).
• What is an example?
• What is an example of interactions that could take place between your kingdom and another corner's kingdom?

3. Environmental Cycles

Objective: Students will demonstrate their knowledge of the cyclical nature of nutrient cycles in the environment.

Corner 1: Water Cycle
Corner 2: Nitrogen Cycle
Corner 3: Carbon Dioxide Cycle

Focus Questions:
- What does this cycle look like? (Draw a picture of it with the other members in your corner.)
- What elements are involved in this cycle?
- Explain the biological significance of the cycle: How does it impact living organisms?
- What would happen if this cycle were disturbed?

4. Mutation Types

Objective: Students will demonstrate how different mutations impact genetic diversity.

Corner 1: Deletion
Corner 2: Nondisjunction
Corner 3: Inversion
Corner 4: Duplication

Focus Questions:
- What is the process that leads to this mutation type?
- What role does meiosis play in this process?
- What are the outcomes of this mutation type?
- Do you think that scientists should be able to alter a mutated chromosome?

Kagan Publishing • 1 (800) 933-2667
www.KaganOnline.com

BIOLOGY
BLACKline Corners

Corners Focus Questions for Macromolecules

*The focus questions below are for use with the following blackline masters.
Ask students focus questions after students have gone to their corners.
Have students pair up to discuss, using Timed Pair Share or RallyRobin.*

1. What biological macromolecule do I represent?
2. What elements make me up?
3. What is my function in living systems?
4. What are three examples of my macromolecule from life?

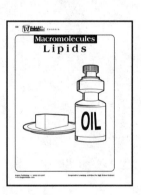
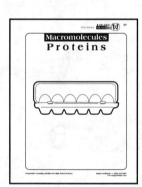
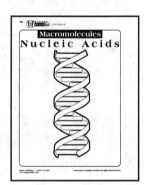

Macromolecules
Carbohydrates

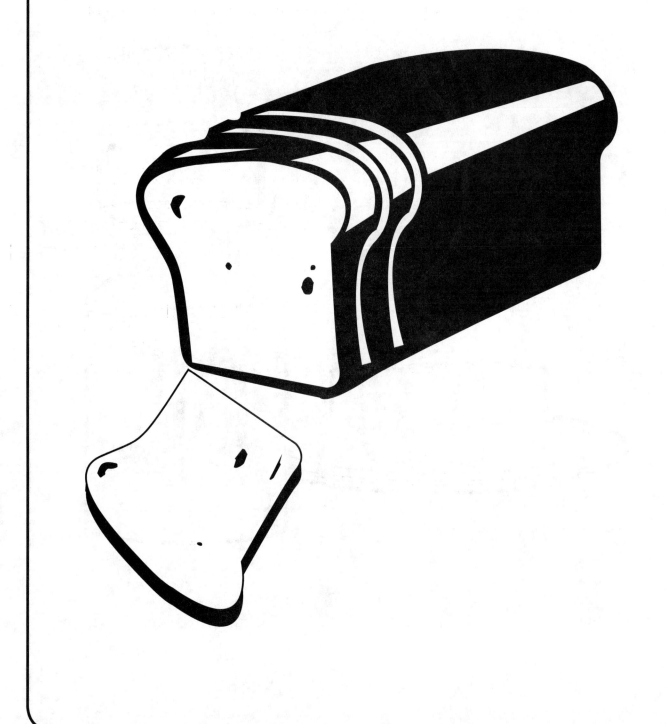

Macromolecules

Lipids

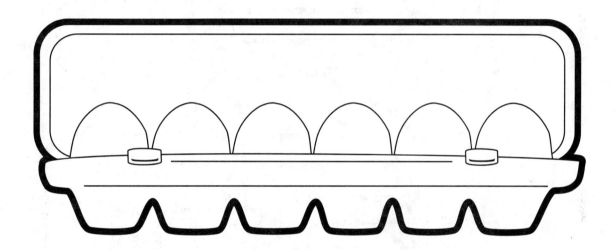

Macromolecules
Proteins

BIOLOGY
BLACKline Corners

Macromolecules

Nucleic Acids

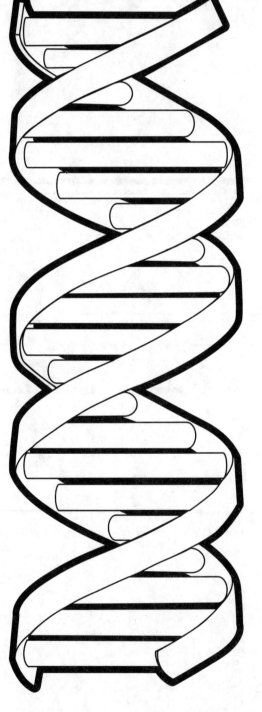

Cooperative Learning Activities For High School Science

Corners Focus Questions for Levels of Organization

The focus questions below are for use with the following blackline masters.
Ask students focus questions after students have gone to their corners.
Have students pair up to discuss, using Timed Pair Share or RallyRobin.

1. What level of organization am I?
2. Many of me together will make up what level?
3. What are three examples of this level of organization in real life?

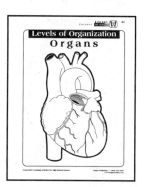
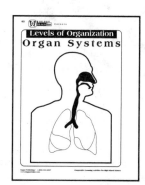
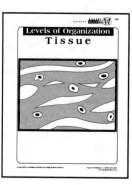

Levels of Organization

Cells

Levels of Organization

Organs

Kagan Publishing • 1 (800) 933-2667
www.KaganOnline.com

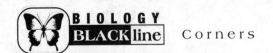

BIOLOGY
BLACKline Corners

Levels of Organization

Organ Systems

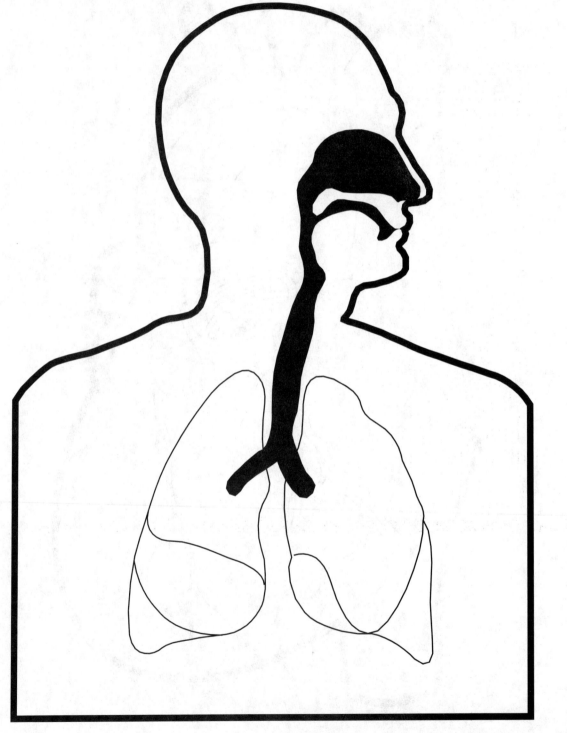

Levels of Organization
Tissue

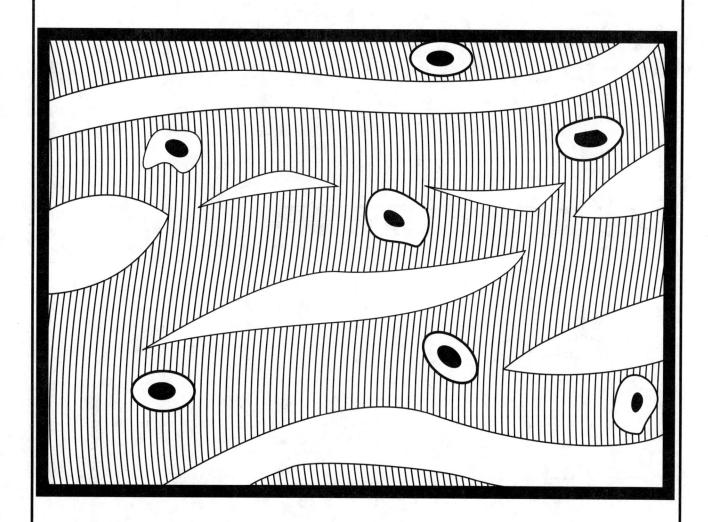

1. Types of Bonds

Objective: Students will recognize the importance and chemical nature of different bond types.

> **Corner 1:** Covalent
> **Corner 2:** Ionic
> **Corner 3:** Hydrogen

Focus Questions:
- How is this bond formed?
- Can you relate the strength of this bond to the other corners?
- From your periodic table, can you pick two elements that would combine to exemplify this bond?
- What are the charges of each element in the compound you made?

2. States of Matter

Objective: Students will be able to identify the states of matter and their molecular interactions.

> **Corner 1:** Solid
> **Corner 2:** Liquid
> **Corner 3:** Gas
> **Corner 4:** Plasma

Focus Questions:
- How do my molecules move? (Demonstrate with your body).
- How does temperature increase affect the kinetic energy of this state of matter?
- What is a common example of this state of matter that is present in the room?

3. Changes of State

Objective: Students will understand the mechanics involved as matter changes states.

    Corner 1: Evaporation
    Corner 2: Condensation
    Corner 3: Freezing
    Corner 4: Melting

Focus Questions:
- What temperature change controls this phase change?
- What do my molecules look like before and after this process? (Draw a picture).
- If your sample was water, what temperature would this process occur at?

4. Alkanes, Alkenes, Alkynes

Objective: Students will recognize the structural differences between the three organic molecules.

    Corner 1: Alkanes
    Corner 2: Alkenes
    Corner 3: Alkynes

Focus Questions:
- What type of covalent bond distinguishes your organic molecule from the other corners?
- What is the structural formula of propane, propene, or propyne (the one for your corner)? Draw it.
- How do the above examples differ from octane, octene, octyne?

5. Solubility and Solutions

Objective: Students will recognize the different states of solubility.

    Corner 1: Saturated Solution
    Corner 2: Unsaturated Solution
    Corner 3: Supersaturated Solution

See Blackline p.71

Focus Questions:
- What is a definition for the scientific term found in your corner? (Write it).
- Look at the solubility curve. Which solution represents the term found in your corner?
- Why? Explain your answer.
- How would the solubility of your solution be impacted if temperature were changed?

*Note to teacher: *You must supply each corner with a solubility curve to examine.*

Corners Focus Questions for Chemical Elements

*The focus questions below are for use with the following blackline masters.
Ask students focus questions after students have gone to their corners.
Have students pair up to discuss, using Timed Pair Share or RallyRobin.*

1. What is my physical state and why?
2. Am I classified as a metal, nonmetal, or metalloid and why?
3. What is another element in the periodic table that has the same charge and belongs to the same family?

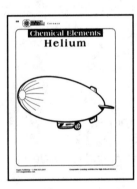

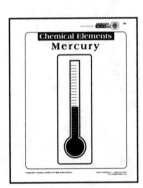

Chemical Elements
Carbon

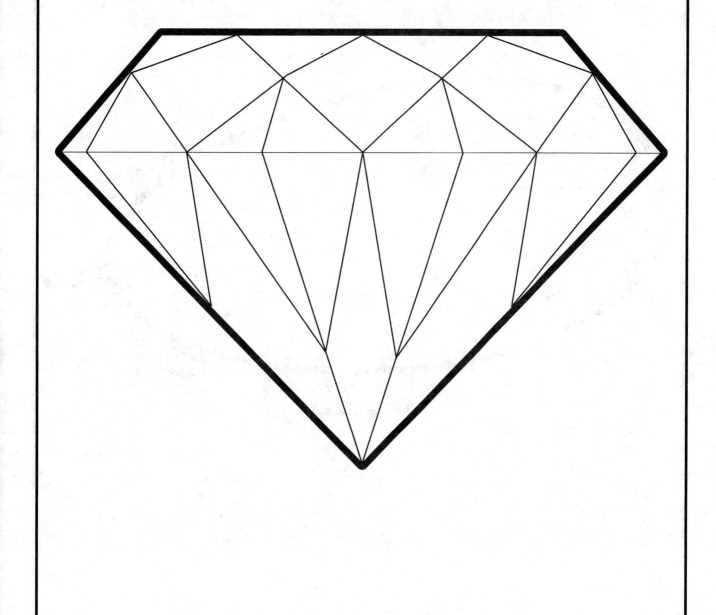

Chemical Elements
Helium

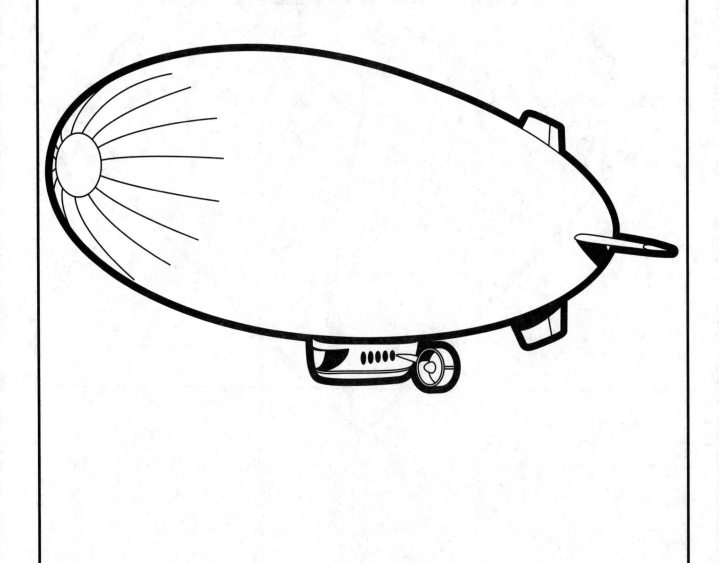

Kagan Publishing • 1 (800) 933-2667
www.KaganOnline.com

Cooperative Learning Activities For High School Science

Chemical Elements
Mercury

CHEMISTRY BLACKline Corners

Chemical Elements
Sodium

Corners Focus Questions for Solubility & Solutions

The focus questions below are for use with the following blackline masters. Ask students focus questions after students have gone to their corners. Have students pair up to discuss, using Timed Pair Share or RallyRobin.

☆ *Teacher must supply each corner with a solubility curve.*

1. What is a definition for the scientific term found in your corner? (Write it).
2. Look at the solubility curve. Which solution represents the term found in your corner?
3. Why? Explain your answer.
4. How would the solubility of your solution be impacted if temperature were changed?

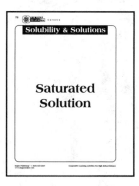
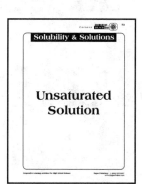
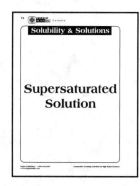

Solubility & Solutions

Saturated Solution

Solubility & Solutions

Unsaturated Solution

Solubility & Solutions

Supersaturated Solution

Corners
Earth Science Activity Ideas

1. Stellar Evolution

Objective: Students will identify the differences between star stages.

    Corner 1: Main Sequence
    Corner 2: Giants
    Corner 3: Birth
    Corner 4: Death

Focus Questions:
- What is the star like in this stage of its life? (Describe it).
- What is my size in comparison to the other corners?
- How is my gravity different from the other corners?
- How does the energy of your star stage compare and contrast to the other corners?

2. Types of Galaxies

Objective: Students will identify the different galaxy types.

    Corner 1: Spiral
    Corner 2: Elliptical
    Corner 3: Irregular

Focus Questions:
- What do I look like? (Draw a picture).
- What color am I usually, and why?
- What is an example of this galaxy?
- Where is this galaxy in relationship to Earth?

3. Plate Boundaries

Objective: Students will understand how plate tectonics function.

Corner 1: Transform
Corner 2: Divergent
Corner 3: Convergent

Focus Questions:
- How do two plates interacting in this manner appear? (Draw a picture).
- What characteristic structures are located at this plate boundary?
- What is an example of this boundary on Earth?

4. Weather Fronts

Objective: Students will be able to describe and forecast weather events.
* Teacher must supply each corner with a weather map.

Corner 1: Cold Front
Corner 2: Warm Front
Corner 3: Occluded Front
Corner 4: Stationary front

Focus Questions:
- What are the characteristics of this front?
- What is the map symbolization for your front? (Draw it).
- What weather is associated with your front?
- Based on the weather map provided, what will the weather be like in your state three days from now?

5. Rock Types

Objective: Students will be able to recognize the three major rock types.

Corner 1: Igneous
Corner 2: Metamorphic
Corner 3: Sedimentary

See Blackline p.82

Focus Questions:
- Where am I usually found?
- What am I composed of?
- How was I formed?
- What is at least one example of a rock of this type?

Corners Focus Questions
for Celestial Bodies

The focus questions below are for use with the following blackline masters. Ask students focus questions after students have gone to their corners. Have students pair up to discuss, using Timed Pair Share or RallyRobin.

1. Where am I usually found?
2. Which other type of body do I usually orbit, or do bodies orbit me?
3. What is one example of each in our solar system, other than Earth?

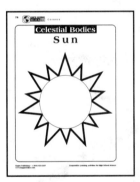

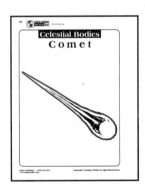

Celestial Bodies

Sun

Celestial Bodies
Moon

Celestial Bodies
Comet

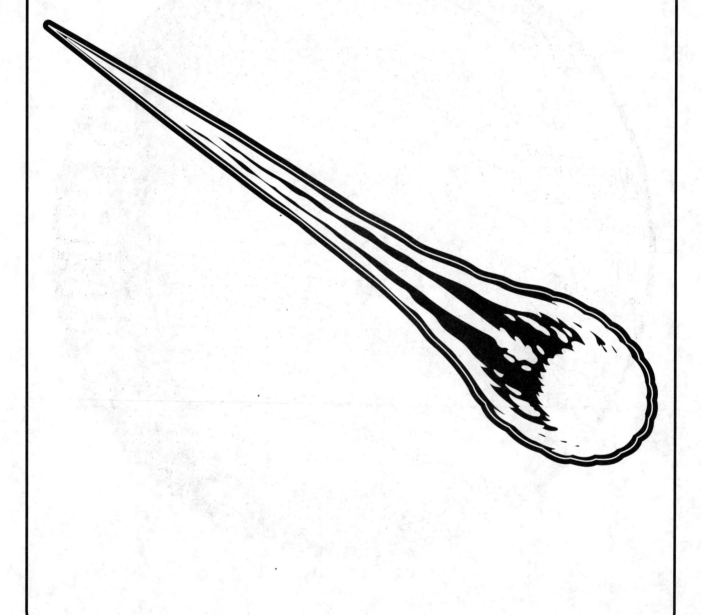

Celestial Bodies
Planet

Corners Focus Questions for Rock Types

The focus questions below are for use with the following blackline masters.
Ask students focus questions after students have gone to their corners.
Have students pair up to discuss, using Timed Pair Share or RallyRobin.

1. Where am I usually found?
2. What am I composed of?
3. How was I formed?
4. What is at least one example of a rock of this type?

Rock Types

Igneous

EARTH SCIENCE
BLACKline Corners

Rock Types

Metamorphic

Rock Types
Sedimentary

1. Types of Waves

Objective: Students will demonstrate an understanding of different wave types.

Corner 1: Light
Corner 2: Sound
Corner 3: Water

Focus Questions:
- How are these waves alike?
- How is your wave different from the other corners?
- What are the parts of your wave? Draw it and label its parts.
- Am I transverse or longitudinal?

2. Electromagnetic Devices

Objective: Students will be able to identify different electromagnetic devices.

Corner 1: Transformer
Corner 2: Generator
Corner 3: Electric Motor

Focus Questions:
- What are the parts of your device?
- What is your device used for?
- What are three common examples of your device?
- What one part is found in all three devices?

3. Temperature Scales

Objective: Students will be able to recognize and interpret different temperature scales.

Corner 1: Celsius
Corner 2: Fahrenheit
Corner 3: Kelvin

Focus Questions:
- What does temperature actually measure?
- How does your temperature scale differ from the other two corners?
- What are the conversion equations from your scale to the other two? (Write them).
- Where is this scale most commonly used?

4. Newton's Laws

Objective: Students will distinguish between the three laws of motion and know how they apply to everyday situations.

Corner 1: Inertia
Corner 2: Momentum
Corner 3: Velocity
Corner 4: Acceleration

Focus Questions:
- What's the definition of your word? Give an example.
- Which of Newton's Laws can control your action?
- How does friction play a role in your action?

Corners Focus Questions for Metric Measurements

The focus questions below are for use with the following blackline masters.
Ask students focus questions after students have gone to their corners.
Have students pair up to discuss, using Timed Pair Share or RallyRobin.

1. What three things in the room would you use this metric measurement for?
2. What measuring tool would be used to gather this information?
3. What is an example of a real life situation where you have seen this measurement being used?

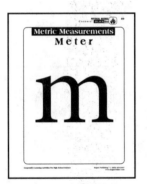

Metric Measurements

Meter

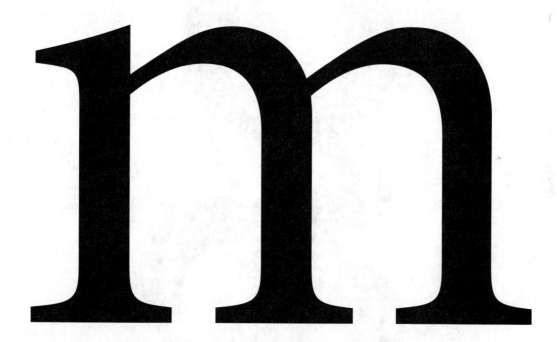

Metric Measurements
Gram

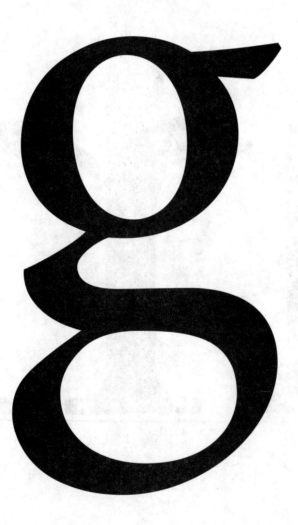

Metric Measurements

Liter

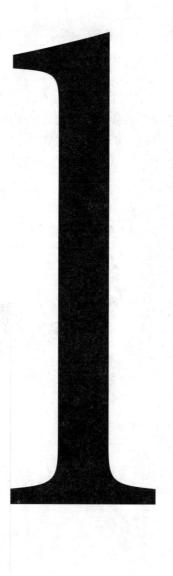

1

PHYSICAL SCIENCE
BLACKline Corners

Corners Focus Questions
for Density

The focus questions below are for use with the following blackline masters.
Ask students focus questions after students have gone to their corners.
Have students pair up to discuss, using Timed Pair Share or RallyRobin.

1. How does the density of the substance from your corner compare to that of water?
2. What would happen to the density of your substance if you doubled the amount of matter?
3. What would happen to the density of your substance if you reduced the volume of the matter by one half?
4. What do you have to do to change the density of a substance?

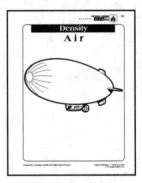

Density
Rock

PHYSICAL SCIENCE
BLACKline Corners

Density

Feather

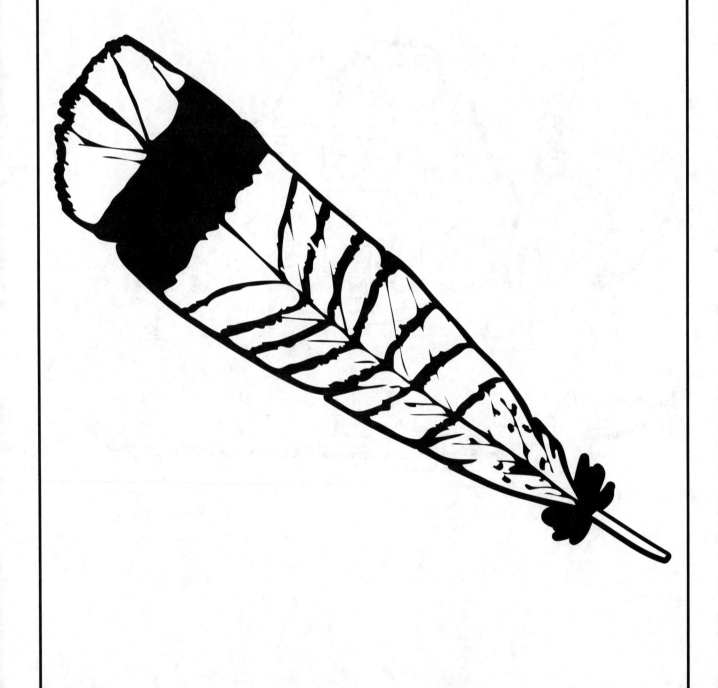

Density
Air

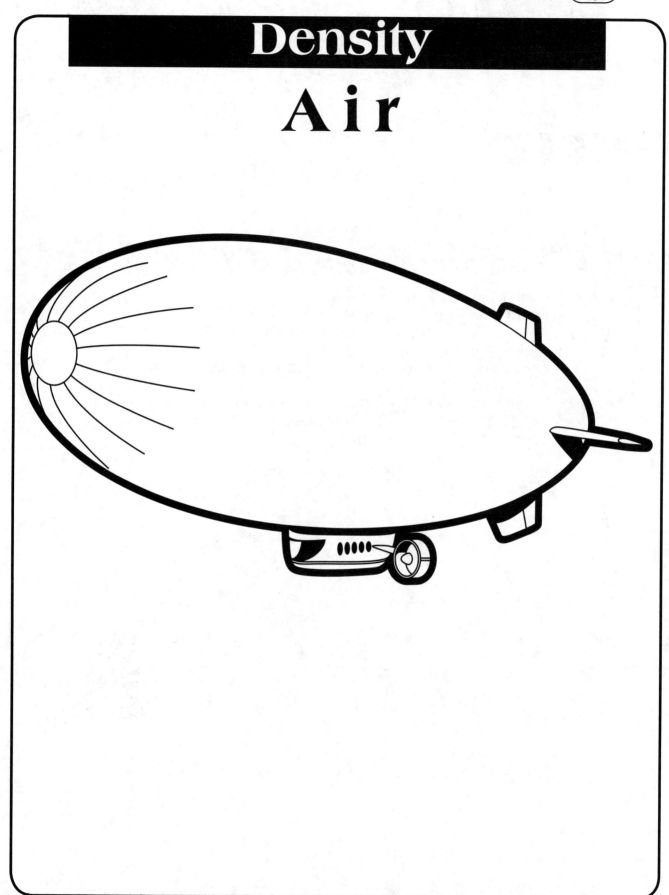

1. Safety

Objective: Students will identify safety protocol and its importance in the lab.

Corner 1: Working With Fire
Corner 2: Working With Dry Chemicals
Corner 3: Working With Solutions
Corner 4: Proper Attire

Focus Questions:
- Why am I important for lab safety?
- What are two examples of something that could happen if my protocol is not followed?
- What safety symbols are associated with this lab protocol? Draw a picture of them.
- What emergency procedure should you follow if my protocol is not followed?

BIOLOGY

PHYSICAL SCIENCE

Mix-N-Match

ENERAL SCIENCE

CHEMISTRY

EARTH SCIENCE

4 Mix-N-Match

Students mix, repeatedly quizzing new partners and trading cards. Afterward, they rush to find a partner with the card that matches theirs.

1 With a card in their hand, each student mixes around the room. Each finds a partner, and quizzes him or her by asking a question relating to their card. (Example: "I have helium. What's the symbol for helium?" or "I have Na, what element do I represent?")

2 Partner answers. Praise or coaching is given.

3 Switch roles: The other partner asks, then praises or coaches.

4 Partners trade cards.

5 Partners split up and repeat Steps 1 through 4 a number of times.

6 Teacher calls "Freeze."

7 Students freeze, hide their cards, and think of their match.

8 Students move to the center of the room, find their match, and quickly move away from the center of the room with their new partner.

Optional: Teacher may post a class graph to record the time it takes for students to find their matching partners. Students try to beat their class record.

Student Instructions:
When I give the signal, you will stand up with your card and find a partner. Use your card to quiz your partner. Then, your partner will quiz you using his/her card. Trade cards and repeat the process with a new partner. We will do several rounds of quizzing and trading. Then I'll call, "Freeze." You will quickly find your partner with a matching card.

Mix-N-Match
Activities & Blacklines

Biology
A. Activity Ideas

B. Blackline Master

Chemistry
A. Activity Ideas

B. Blackline Master

Earth Science
A. Activity Ideas

B. Blackline Master

Physical Science
A. Activity Ideas

B. Blackline Master

General Science
A. Activity Ideas

B. Blackline Master

1. Phases of the Cell Cycle

Objective: Students will describe and identify the phases in the cell cycle.

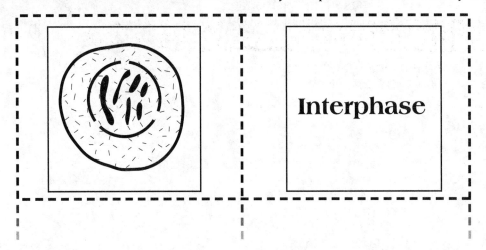

2. Identification of Organ Functions

Objective: Students will match organs to their functions.

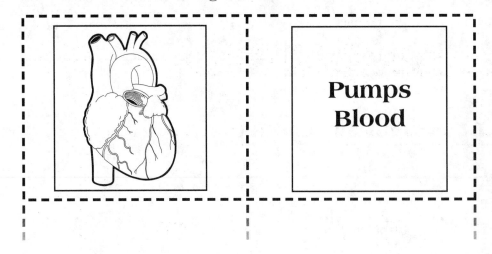

3. Identification of Flower Parts

Objective: Students will identify and recognize flower parts and functions.

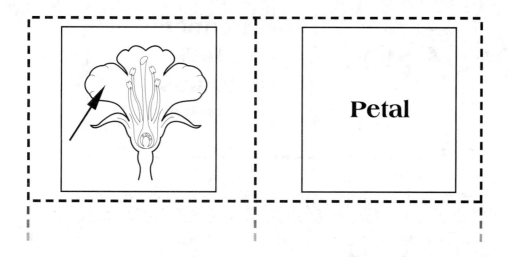

Petal

4. Parts of a Microscope

Objective: Students will be able to identify and know the uses of the microscope parts.

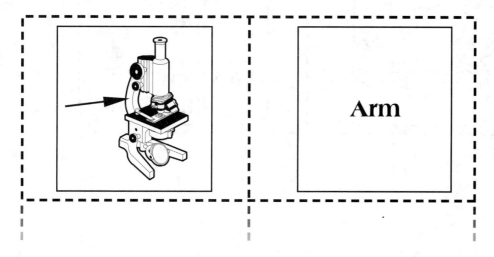

Arm

5. Macromolecules/Food

Objective: Students will be able to identify and know the uses of the macromolecules/food.

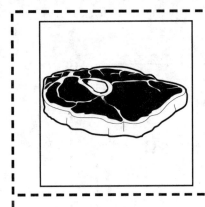

I contain
high
amounts of
protein

6. Classification

Objective: Students will match animals to their classification.

I belong to
the
_____
phylum of
life

7. DNA

Objective: Students will match terms associated with DNA and the DNA code to their symbols.

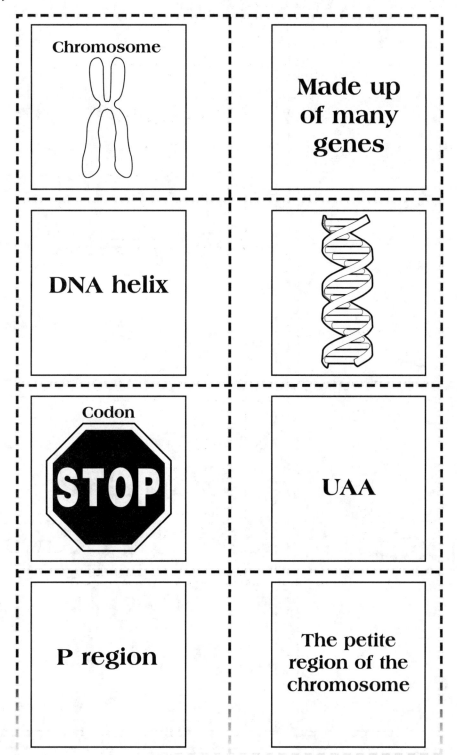

Mix-N-Match
Sample Cards
Digestion

Teeth	Mastication of food
Pepsin	Enzyme that breaks down protein

Mix-N-Match
Sample Cards
Digestion

Stomach	**Responsible for the major physical breakdown of food**
Pancreas	**Secretes insulin**

Mix-N-Match
Sample Cards
Digestion

Liver	**Secretes bile**
Gall Bladder	**Stores bile**

Mix-N-Match
Sample Cards
Digestion

Small Intestine	**Absorbs nutrients**
Villi	**Increases surface area**

Mix-N-Match
Sample Cards
Digestion

Bile Duct

Connects gall bladder to the small intestine

HCl

Keeps pH low in the stomach

Mix-N-Match
Sample Cards
Digestion

Large Intestine	**Absorbs H$_2$O**
Rectum	**Terminal portion of the colon**

Mix-N-Match
Sample Cards
Digestion

Salivary Glands	**Secretes amylase**
Appendix	**Vestigial organ**

Mix-N-Match
Sample Cards
Digestion

Epiglottis

Cartilaginous flap

Peristalsis

Contraction that pushes food down the digestive tract

Mix-N-Match
Sample Cards
Digestion

Small Intestine	**Digests lipids and carbohydrates**
Tongue	**Moves food in the process of swallowing**

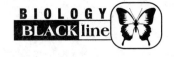

Mix-N-Match
Sample Cards
Digestion

Esophagus	The tube through which food passes from the pharynx to the stomach
Colon	The part of the large intestine extending from the cecum to the rectum

1. Identification of Polyatomic Ions

Objective: Students will be able to identify polyatomic ions.

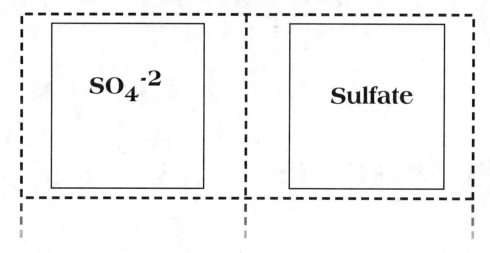

$$SO_4^{-2}$$

Sulfate

2. Atomic Structure

Objective: Students will review the periodic table related to atomic structure.

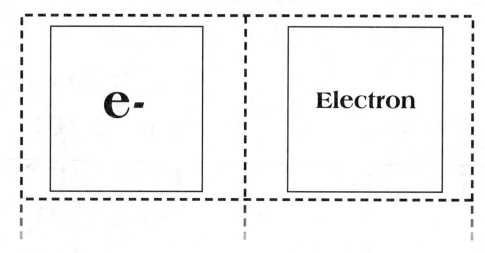

e-

Electron

3. Identification of Compounds

Objective: Students will recognize the symbolic form of compounds.

Al(OH)$_3$

Aluminum Hydroxide

4. Reaction Types

Objective: Students will be able to identify the different types of possible reactions.

$$H_2 + O_2 \longrightarrow H_2O$$

Composition or synthesis

5. Elements

Objective: Students will be able to identify the different types of elements.

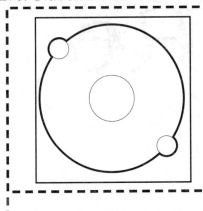

I belong to the noble gas family

Mix-N-Match
Sample Cards
Elements

Calcium

Ca

Helium

He

Mix-N-Match
Sample Cards
Elements

Nitrogen	**N**
Potassium	**K**

Mix-N-Match
Sample Cards
Elements

Sodium

Na

Silver

Ag

Mix-N-Match
Sample Cards
Elements

Gold

Au

Lead

Pb

Mix-N-Match
Sample Cards
Elements

Sulfur

S

Magnesium

Mg

Mix-N-Match
Sample Cards
Elements

Tungsten

W

Manganese

Mn

Mix-N-Match
Sample Cards
Elements

Hydrogen

H

Oxygen

O

Mix-N-Match
Sample Cards
Elements

Carbon

C

Neon

Ne

Mix-N-Match
Sample Cards
Elements

Chlorine	**Cl**
Fluorine	**F**

Kagan Publishing • 1 (800) 933-2667
www.KaganOnline.com

Cooperative Learning Activities For High School Science

Mix-N-Match
Sample Cards
Elements

Aluminum	**Al**
Phosphorus	**P**

1. Ocean Floor Features

Objective: Students will identify the region of the world with its characteristic ocean floor feature.

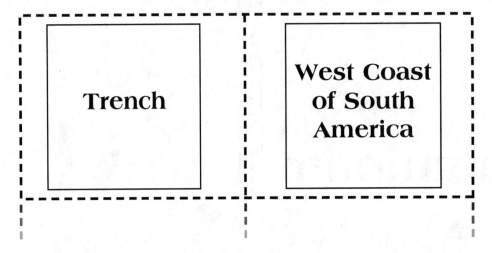

2. Identification of Weather Terms

Objective: Students will identify the weather system and match it with its name or type of weather associated with it.

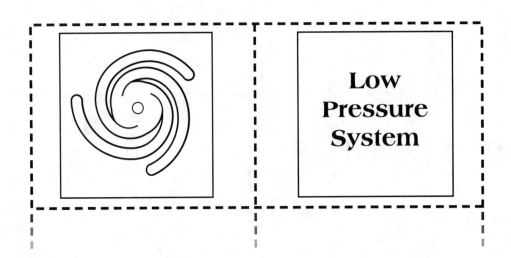

3. Identification of Planets

Objective: Students will match a fact about a planet with the name or picture of the planet.

Visible surface has a large red storm.	

4. Identification of Stars and Constellations

Objective: Students will match pictures or facts with different celestial bodies and constellations in the universe.

Orion, The Great Hunter	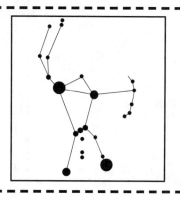

Mix-N-Match
Sample Cards
The Atmosphere

Smog	**A layer of trapped pollutants**
High Pressure	**Condition associated with nice weather**

Mix-N-Match
Sample Cards
The Atmosphere

Stratus Cloud

A large rain-producing cloud

Cumulonimbus Cloud

A thunderhead cloud

Kagan Publishing • 1 (800) 933-2667
www.KaganOnline.com

Mix-N-Match
Sample Cards
The Atmosphere

Cirrus
Cloud

High,
wispy
cloud

Cumulus
Cloud

Big,
cotton ball
cloud

Mix-N-Match
Sample Cards
The Atmosphere

Air Mass

Body of air with uniform temperature and moisture

Front

A boundary between two different air masses

Mix-N-Match
Sample Cards
The Atmosphere

Ozone	**O$_3$**
Barometric	**Pressure of the air**

Kagan Publishing • 1 (800) 933-2667
www.KaganOnline.com

Cooperative Learning Activities For High School Science

Mix-N-Match
Sample Cards
The Atmosphere

Mesosphere	**The layer of the atmosphere that is the coldest**
Thermosphere	**The farthest layer from Earth**

Mix-N-Match
Sample Cards
The Atmosphere

Troposphere	**The layer of the atmosphere closest to the Earth's surface**
Stratosphere	**The layer that contains the ozone layer**

Mix-N-Match
Sample Cards
The Atmosphere

Stationary Front

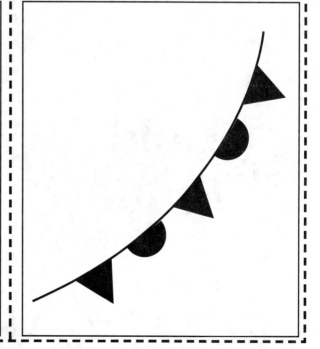

Occluded Front

Mix-N-Match
Sample Cards
The Atmosphere

Warm Front

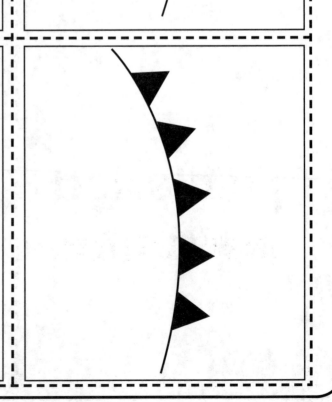

Cold Front

Mix-N-Match
Sample Cards
The Atmosphere

Barometer	**An instrument used to measure barometric pressure**
Low Pressure	**Condition associated with bad weather (precipitation)**

1. Simple Machines

Objective: Students will be able to distinguish between the different simple machines and describe the features of each.

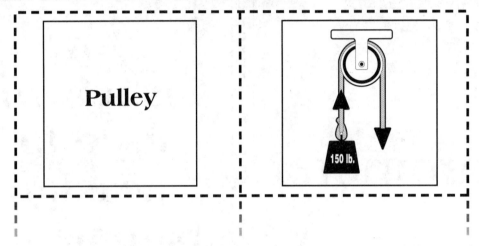

2. Formula Review

Objective: Students will identify various formulas used for quantitative analysis.

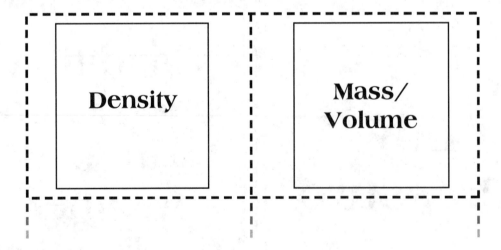

3. Circuit Parts and Features

Objective: Students will recognize circuit diagram parts by matching a part with its drawing.

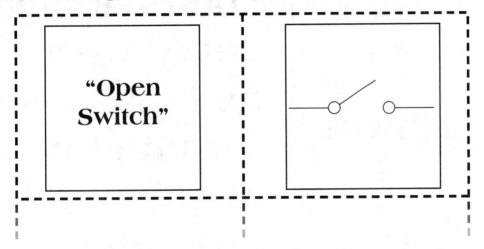

4. Electromagnetic Spectrum

Objective: Students will match a wavelength of the spectrum with an example of its use.

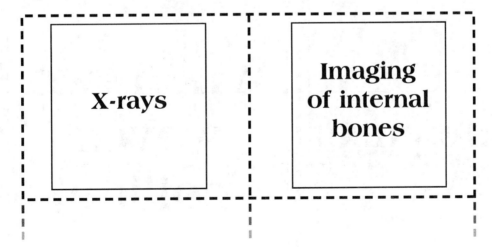

Mix-N-Match
Sample Cards
Waves

Refraction	**The bending of a wave as it passes from one medium to another**
Interference	**When two waves collide**

Mix-N-Match
Sample Cards
Waves

Reflection	**Bouncing back upon striking a boundary**
Diffraction	**Bending of a wave as it passes an edge or an opening**

Mix-N-Match
Sample Cards
Waves

Speed	λ/T
Gamma Rays	**Highest energy wave**

Mix-N-Match
Sample Cards
Waves

Wavelength	λ
Frequency	**1/T**

Mix-N-Match
Sample Cards
Waves

Longitudinal Wave
(definition)

A wave that produces a parallel disturbance

Period

The time required for one wavelength to pass a given point

Mix-N-Match
Sample Cards
Waves

Transverse Wave
(definition)

A wave that produces a perpendicular disturbance

Electromagnetic Wave

A wave that does not require a medium

Mix-N-Match
Sample Cards
Waves

Medium	**Matter that a wave travels through**
Mechanical Wave	**A wave that requires a medium**

Mix-N-Match
Sample Cards
Waves

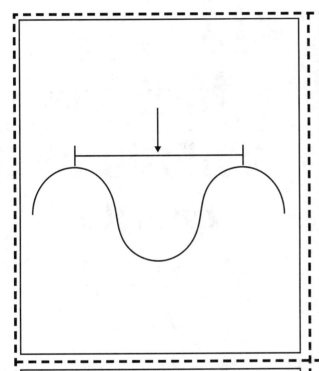

This is the wavelength

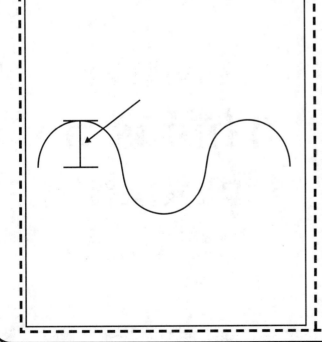

This is the amplitude

Mix-N-Match
Sample Cards
Waves

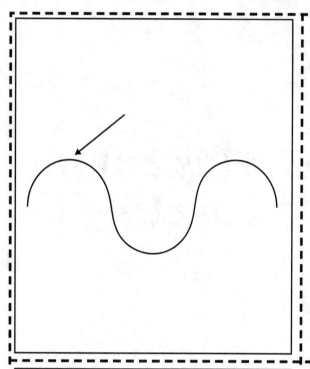

This is a crest

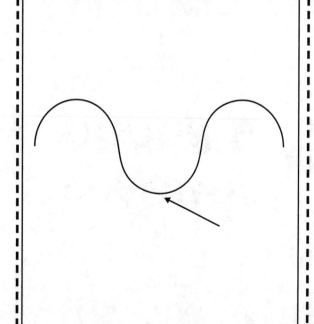

This is a trough

Mix-N-Match
Sample Cards
Waves

Transverse Wave
(example)

An ocean wave

Longitudinal Wave
(example)

A sound wave

1. Identification of Lab Equipment

Objective: Students will work to identify laboratory equipment.

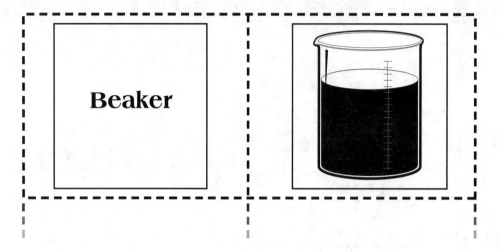

2. Identification of Safety Symbols

Objective: Students will review the essential safety symbols needed for laboratory work.

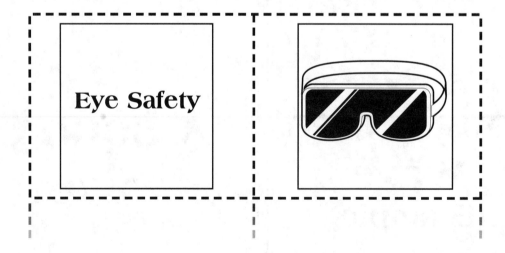

3. Lab Procedural Rules/Techniques

Objective: Students will review standard laboratory practices and procedures.

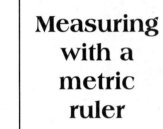

Measuring
with a
metric
ruler

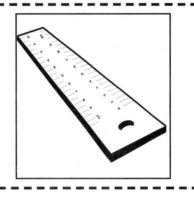

Mix-N-Match
Blank Template

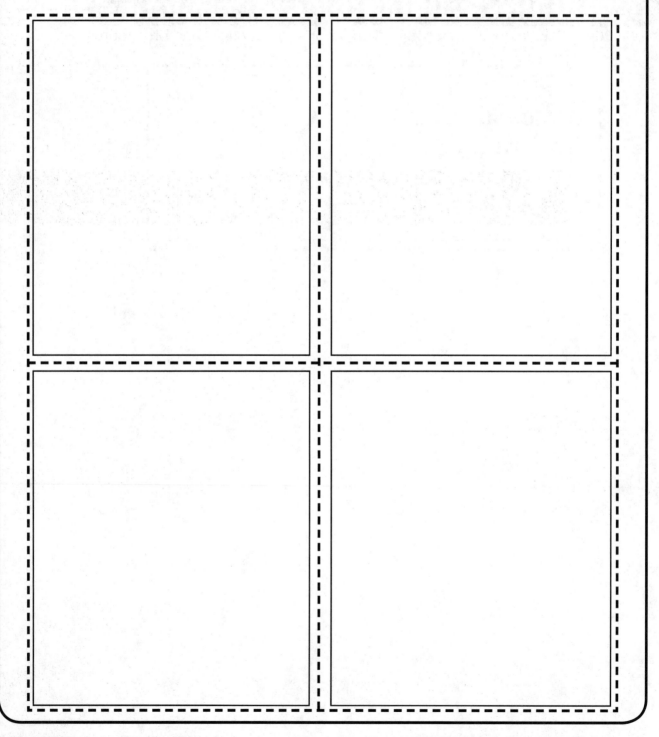

Word Webbing

PHYSICAL SCIENCE

BIOLOGY

ENERAL SCIENCE

CHEMISTRY

EARTH SCIENCE

5 Word Webbing

Students each write in their own color on a team word web which includes a main idea, core concepts, supporting details, and bridges.

1 Teacher announces the main idea.

2 One teammate writes the main idea in the center of the team paper.

3 Teammates RoundTable core concepts. Each teammate writes a core concept around the main idea and connects it to the main idea with a line or arrow.

4 The team has a free-for-all. In their unique colors, teammates add details and make bridges between related ideas.

Student Instructions:
In a minute, I am going to give you a topic. Write that topic in the center of your team paper. Then, in your unique color, each of you will write one core concept relating to that central topic and connect it with a line or arrow to that topic. Then, you will have time to add as many ideas and details to your team word web as you can. You can use words, symbols, arrows, and simple illustrations to best capture the essence and details of the topic and the interrelation of its parts.

Word Webbing
Activities & Blacklines

Biology

Chemistry

Earth Science

Physical Science

General Science

Word Webbing
Biology Activity Ideas

1. Elements Essential for Life

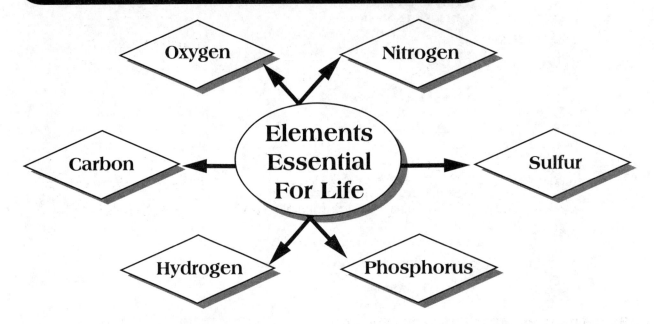

Oxygen

Nitrogen

Carbon

Elements Essential For Life

Sulfur

Hydrogen

Phosphorus

2. The Cell Theory

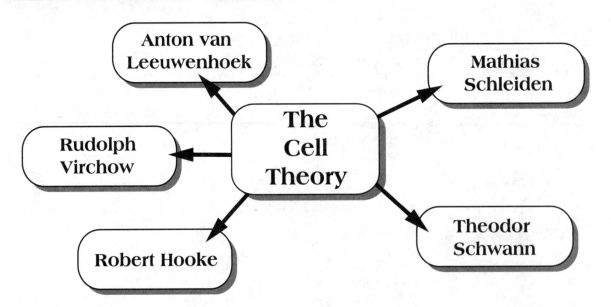

Anton van Leeuwenhoek

Mathias Schleiden

Rudolph Virchow

The Cell Theory

Robert Hooke

Theodor Schwann

3. Classification of Plants

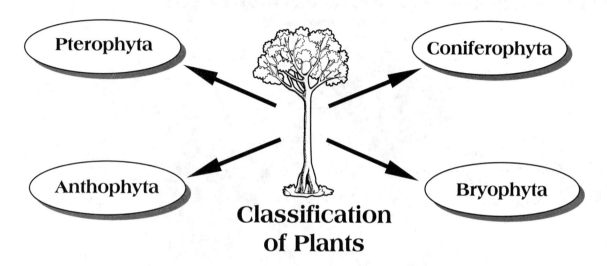

Pterophyta

Coniferophyta

Anthophyta

Bryophyta

**Classification
of Plants**

4. Human Evolution

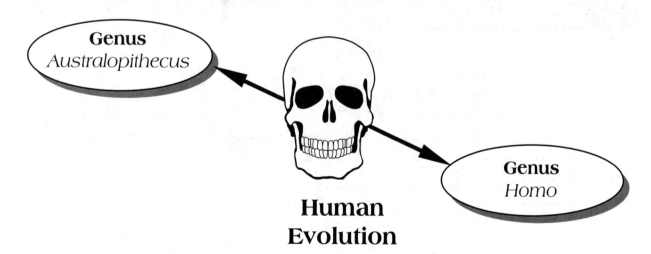

Genus
Australopithecus

Genus
Homo

**Human
Evolution**

Energy Flow in an Ecosystem

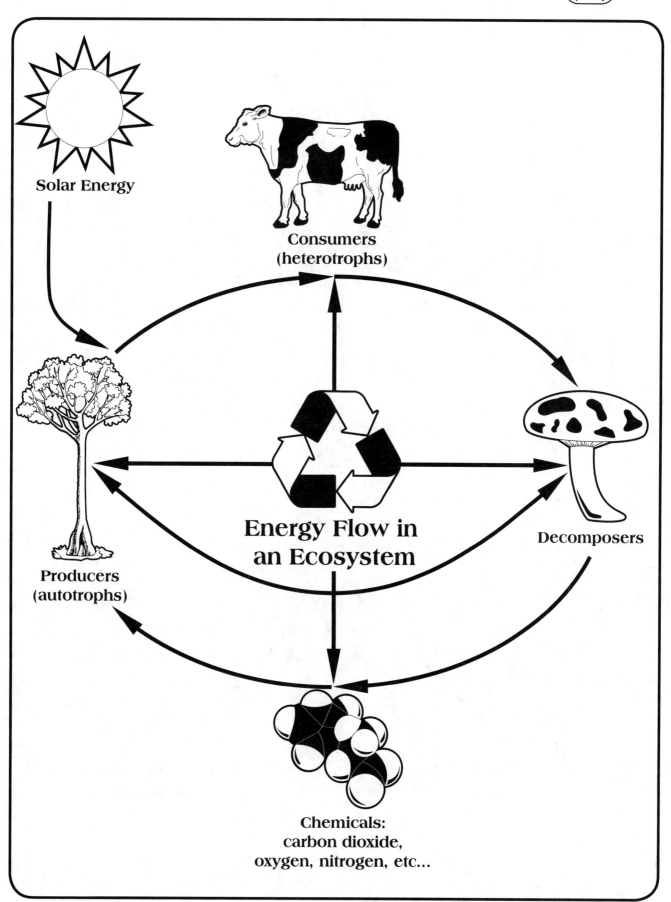

Solar Energy

Consumers
(heterotrophs)

Energy Flow in
an Ecosystem

Producers
(autotrophs)

Decomposers

Chemicals:
carbon dioxide,
oxygen, nitrogen, etc...

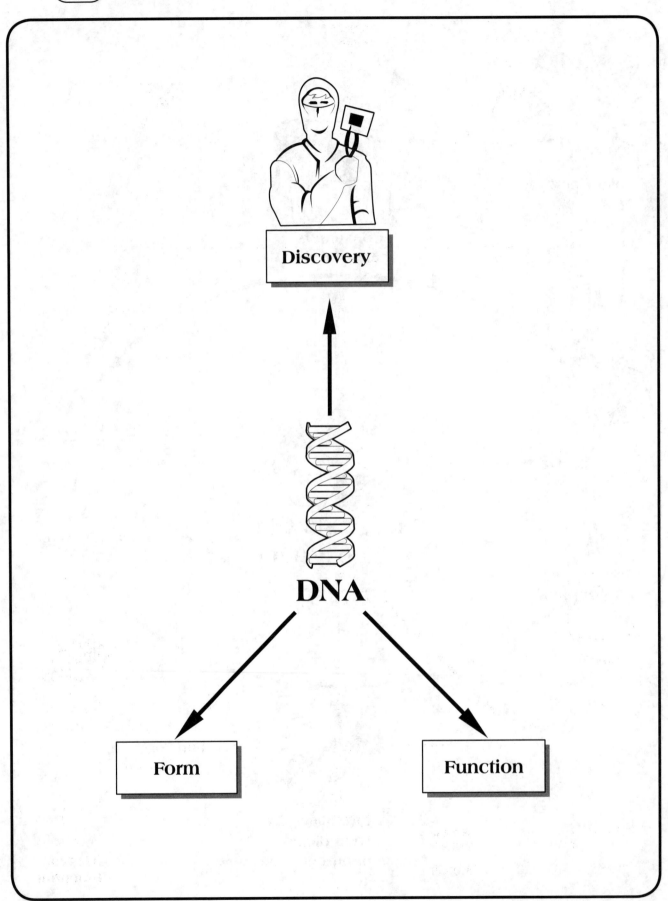

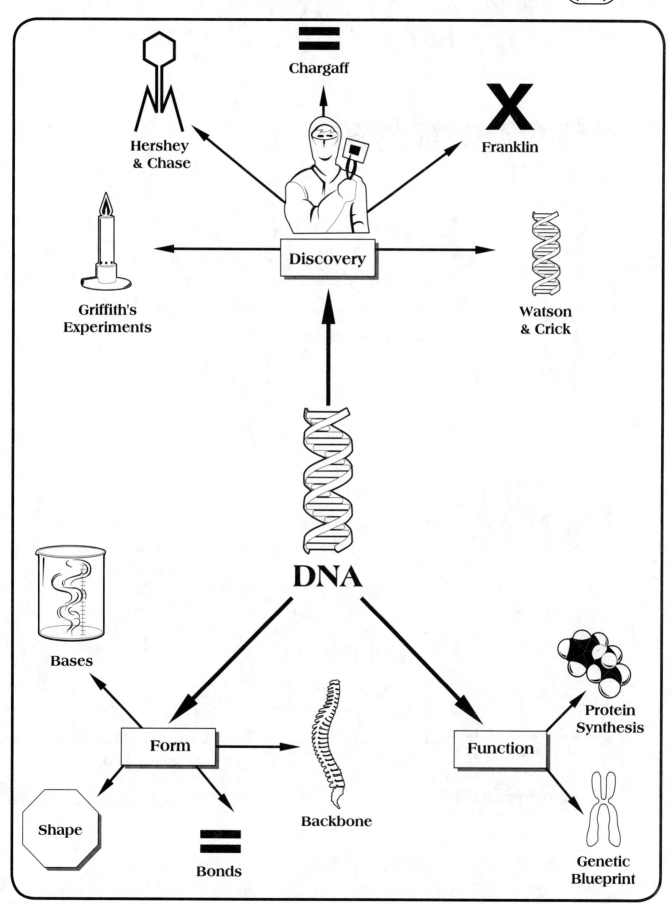

Chargaff

Hershey
& Chase

Franklin

Discovery

Griffith's
Experiments

Watson
& Crick

DNA

Bases

Form

Function

Protein
Synthesis

Shape

Backbone

Bonds

Genetic
Blueprint

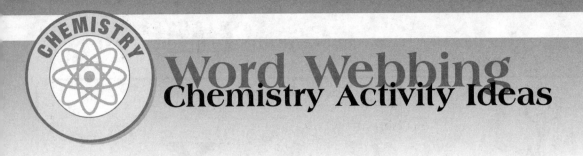

Word Webbing
Chemistry Activity Ideas

1. Phases of Matter

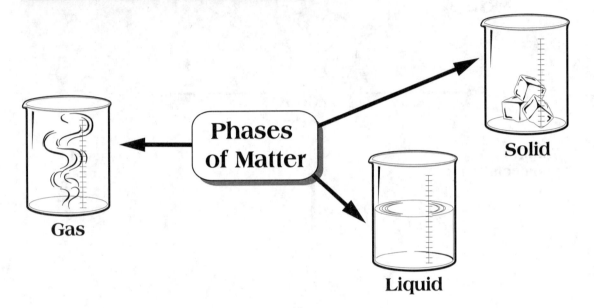

Phases of Matter

Gas

Solid

Liquid

2. Solutions

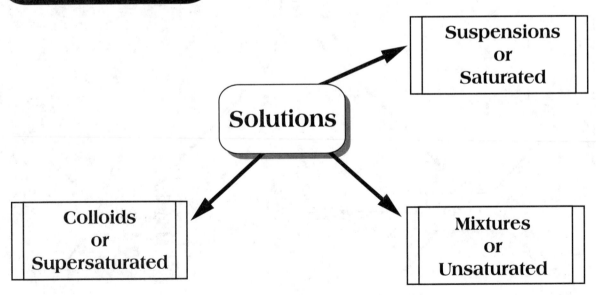

Solutions

Suspensions or Saturated

Colloids or Supersaturated

Mixtures or Unsaturated

3. pH

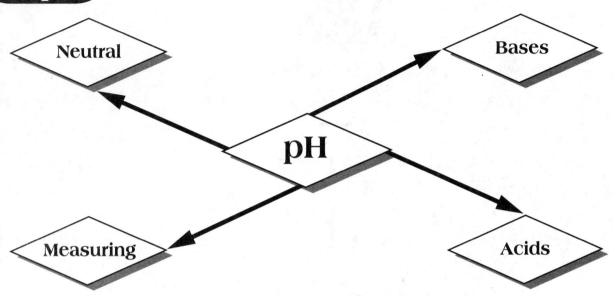

4. Gas Laws

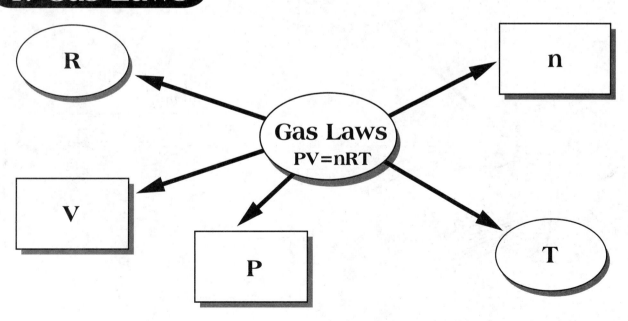

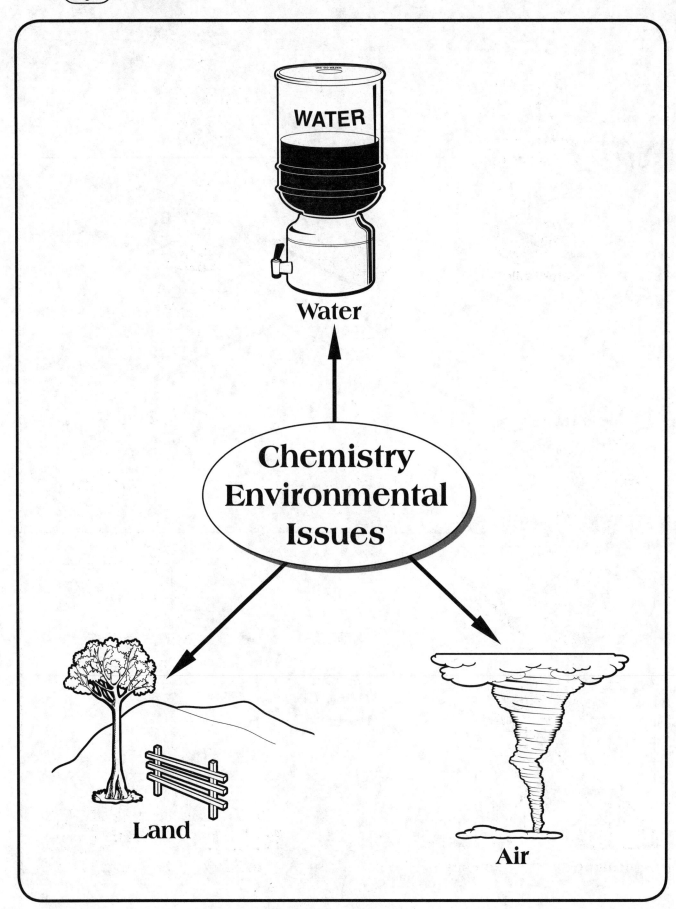

WATER

Water

Chemistry Environmental Issues

Land

Air

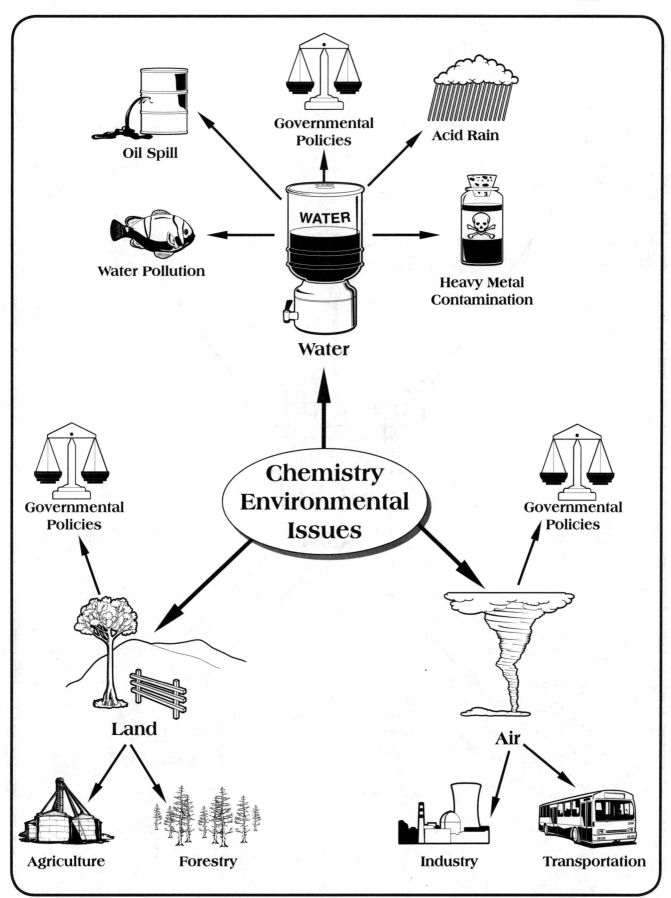

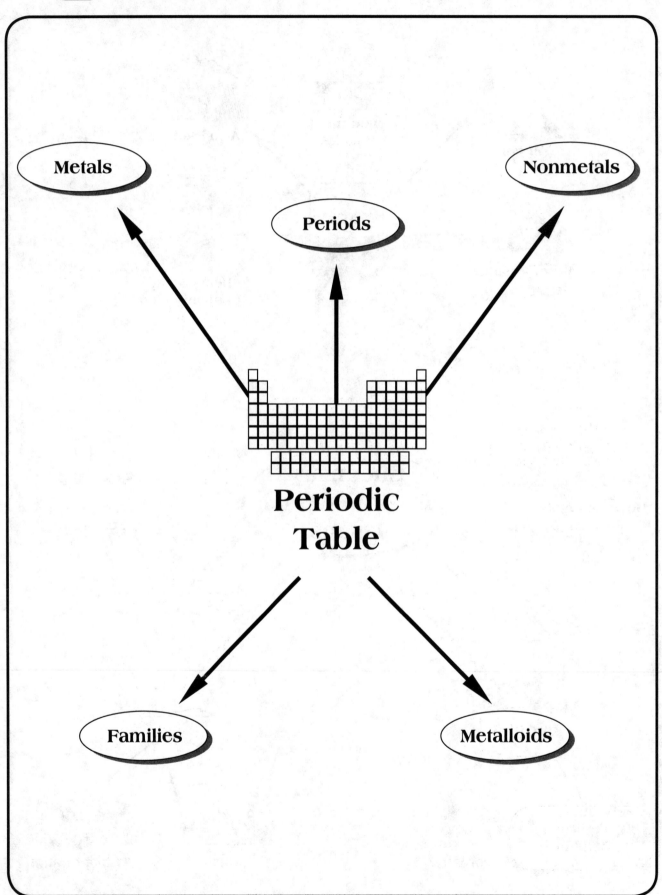

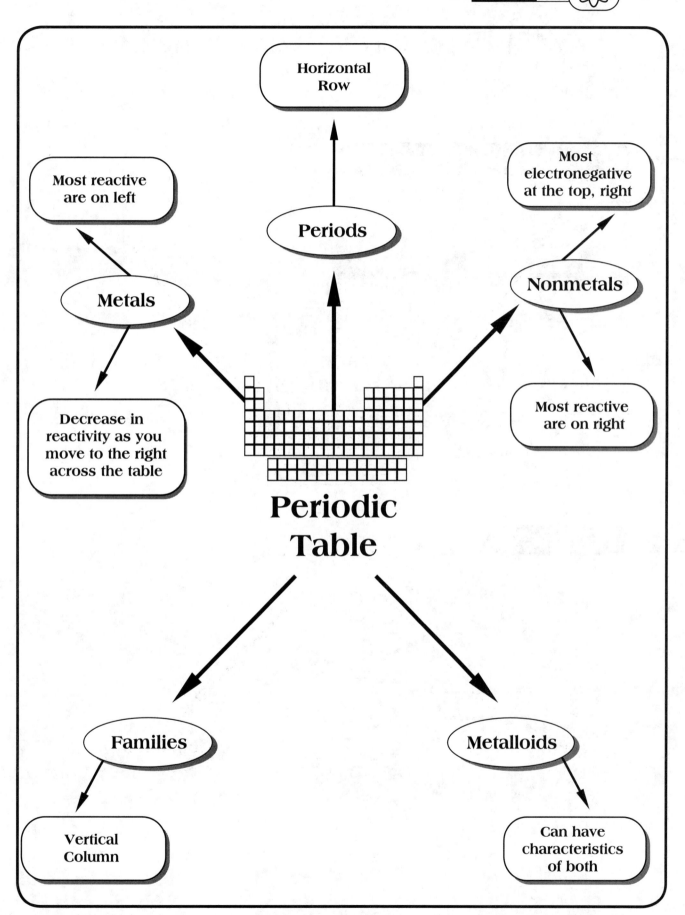

Horizontal Row

Most reactive are on left

Periods

Most electronegative at the top, right

Metals

Nonmetals

Decrease in reactivity as you move to the right across the table

Most reactive are on right

Periodic Table

Families

Metalloids

Vertical Column

Can have characteristics of both

1. Layers of the Earth

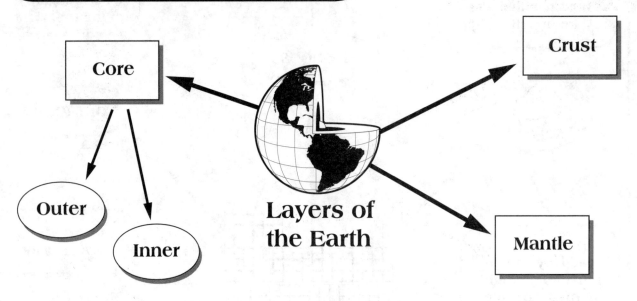

Core

Crust

Outer

Inner

Layers of
the Earth

Mantle

2. Tides

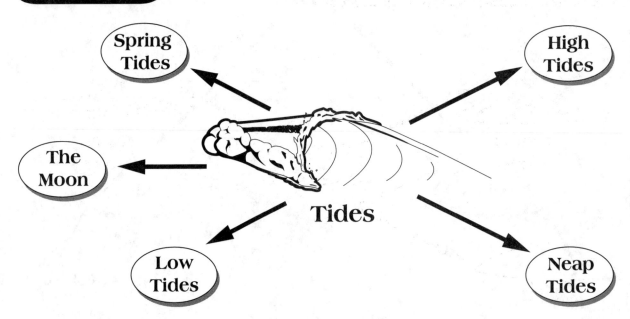

Spring
Tides

High
Tides

The
Moon

Tides

Low
Tides

Neap
Tides

3. Seasons

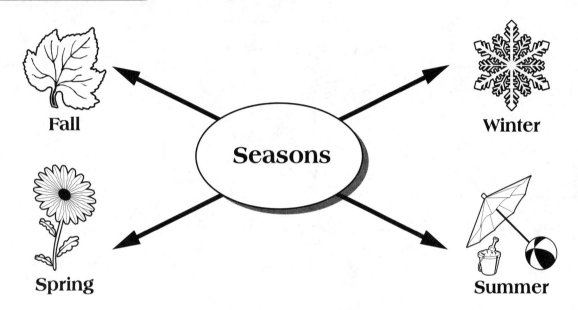

Fall

Seasons

Winter

Spring

Summer

4. Types of Volcanoes

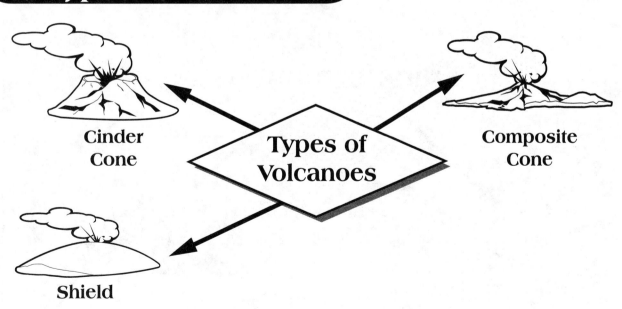

Cinder
Cone

Types of
Volcanoes

Composite
Cone

Shield

The Rock Cycle

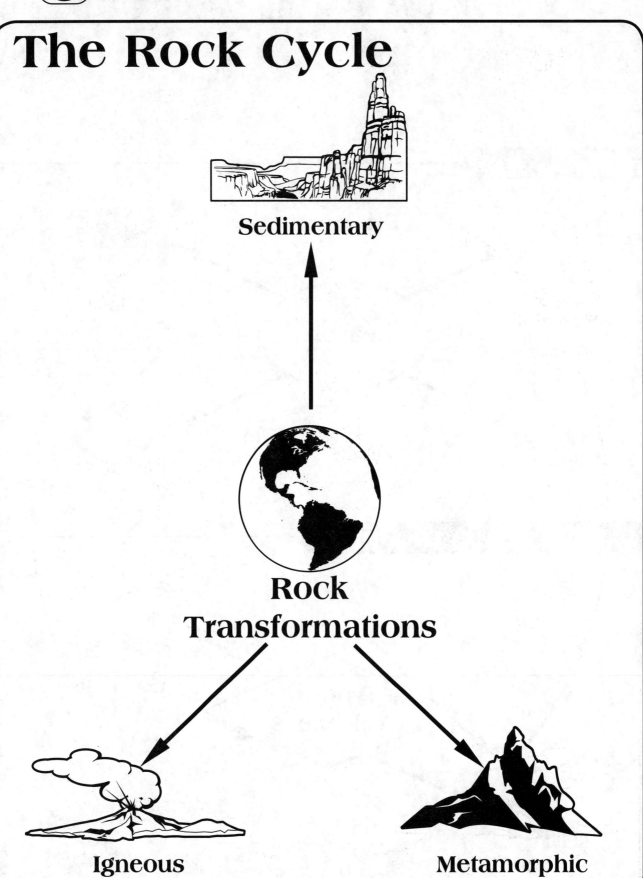

Sedimentary

Rock
Transformations

Igneous

Metamorphic

The Rock Cycle

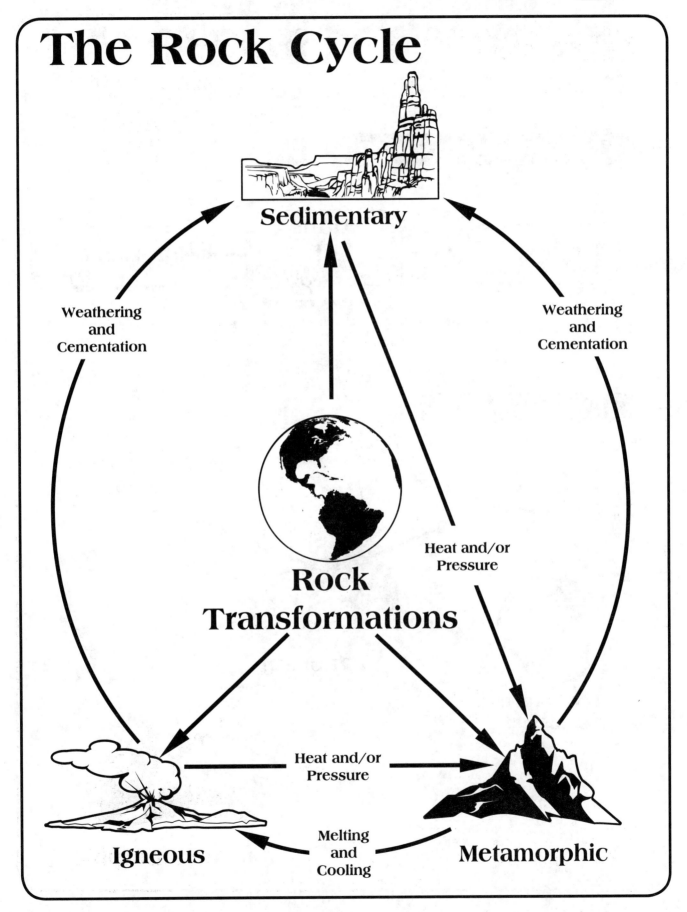

Sedimentary

Weathering and Cementation

Weathering and Cementation

Rock Transformations

Heat and/or Pressure

Heat and/or Pressure

Igneous

Melting and Cooling

Metamorphic

1. Forms of Energy

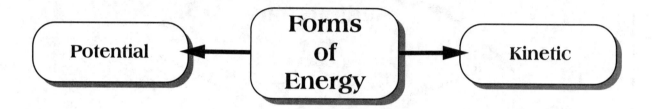

| Potential | ← | Forms of Energy | → | Kinetic |

2. Magnetism

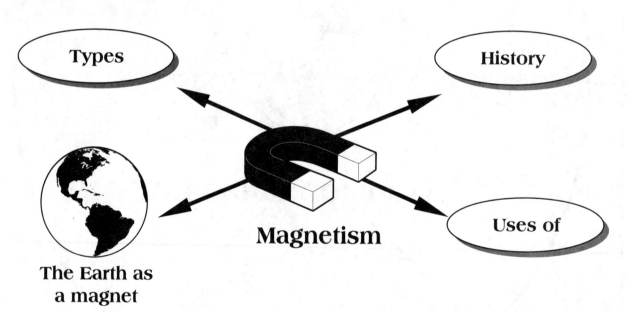

Types

History

The Earth as a magnet

Magnetism

Uses of

3. Mirrors

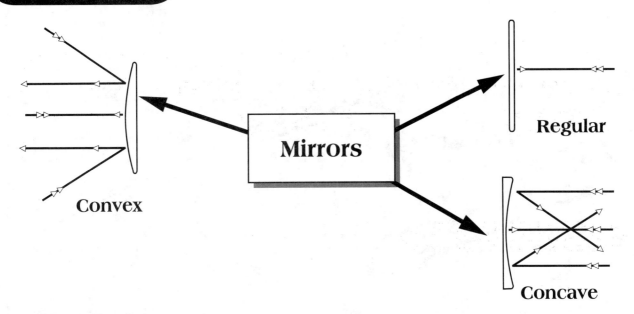

Convex

Mirrors

Regular

Concave

4. Alternative Energy Sources

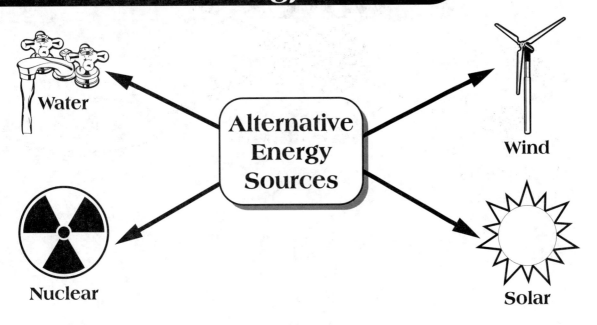

Water

Alternative Energy Sources

Wind

Nuclear

Solar

Kagan Publishing • 1 (800) 933-2667
www.KaganOnline.com

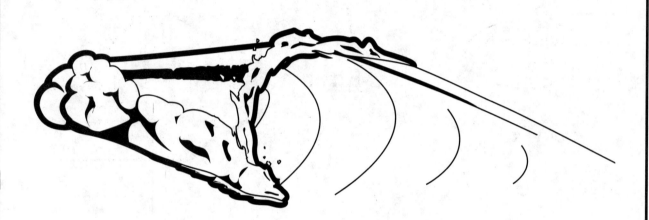

Waves

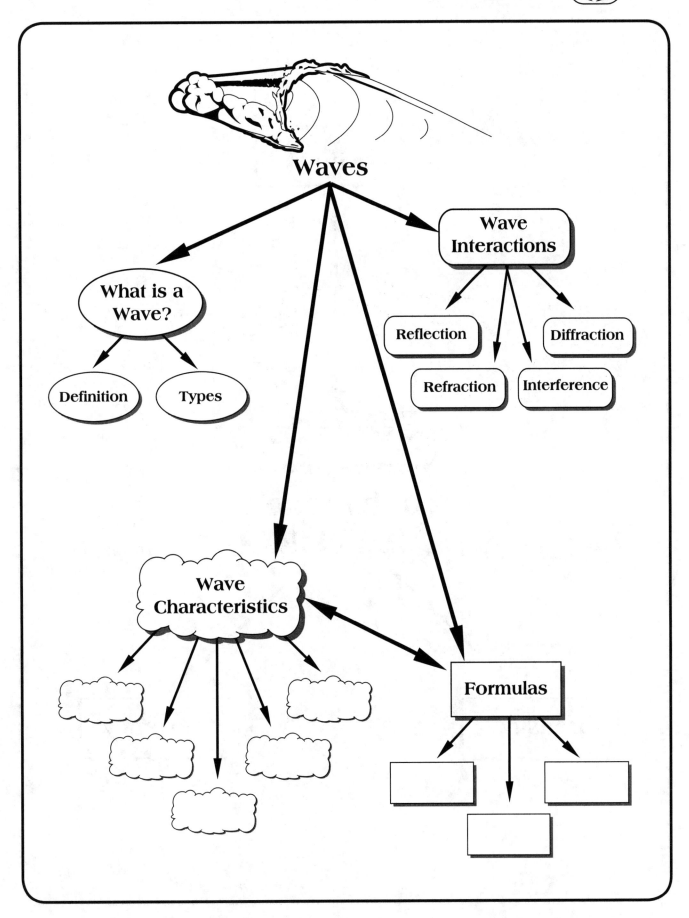

Waves

What is a Wave?

Definition   Types

Wave Interactions

Reflection   Diffraction

Refraction   Interference

Wave Characteristics

Formulas

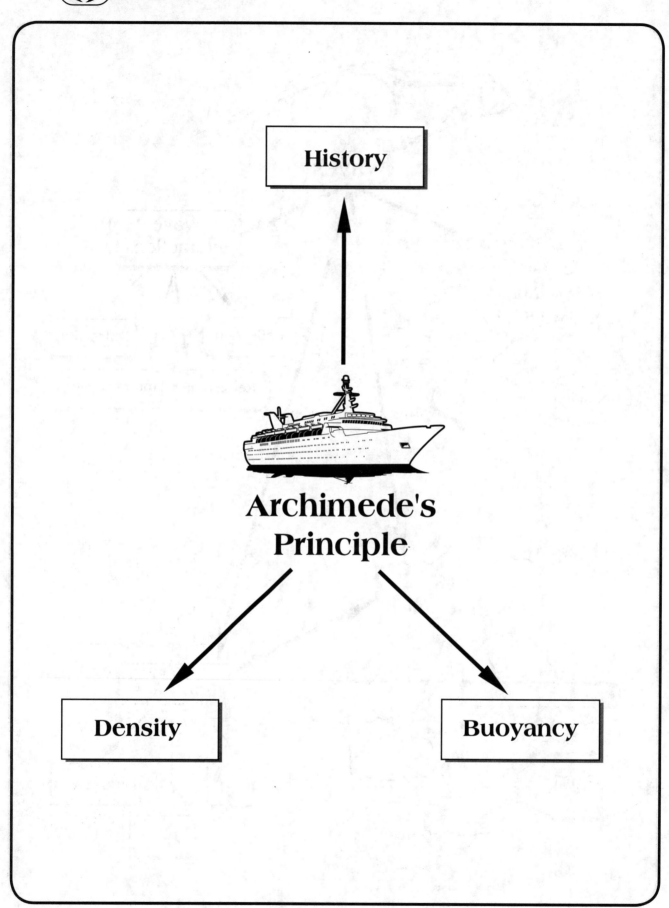

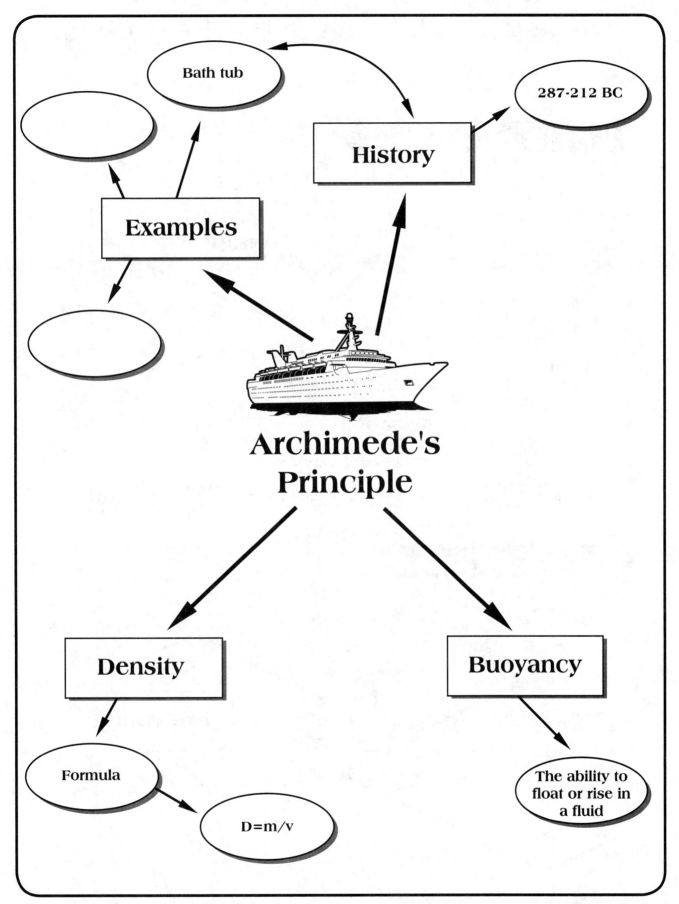

Bath tub

History

287-212 BC

Examples

Archimede's
Principle

Density

Buoyancy

Formula

D=m/v

The ability to
float or rise in
a fluid

Word Webbing
General Science Activity Ideas

1. Lab Equipment

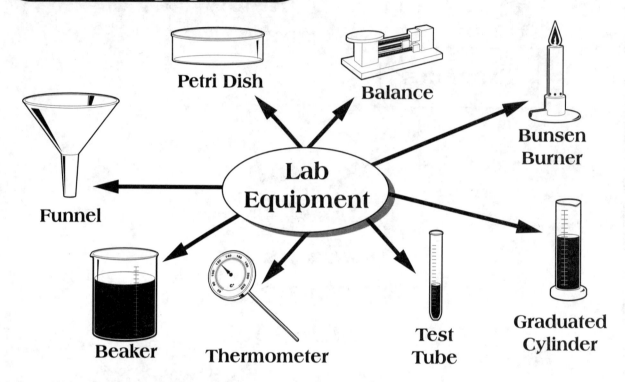

Petri Dish

Balance

Bunsen Burner

Funnel

Lab Equipment

Beaker

Thermometer

Test Tube

Graduated Cylinder

2. Unit Prefixes

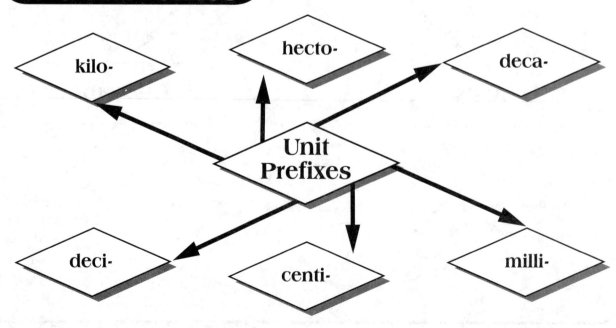

kilo-

hecto-

deca-

Unit Prefixes

deci-

centi-

milli-

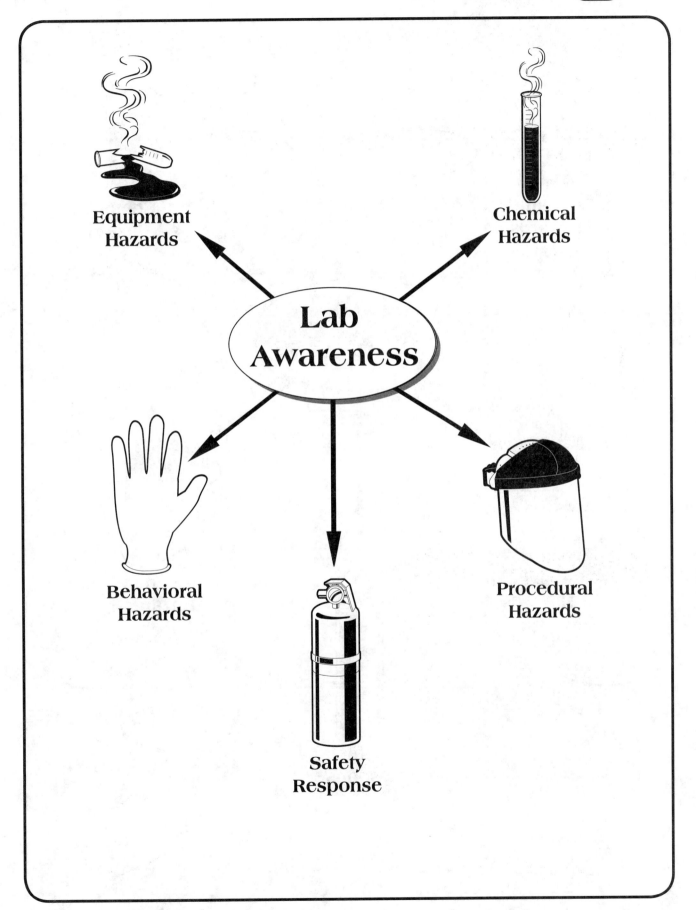

Equipment
Hazards

Chemical
Hazards

Lab
Awareness

Behavioral
Hazards

Safety
Response

Procedural
Hazards

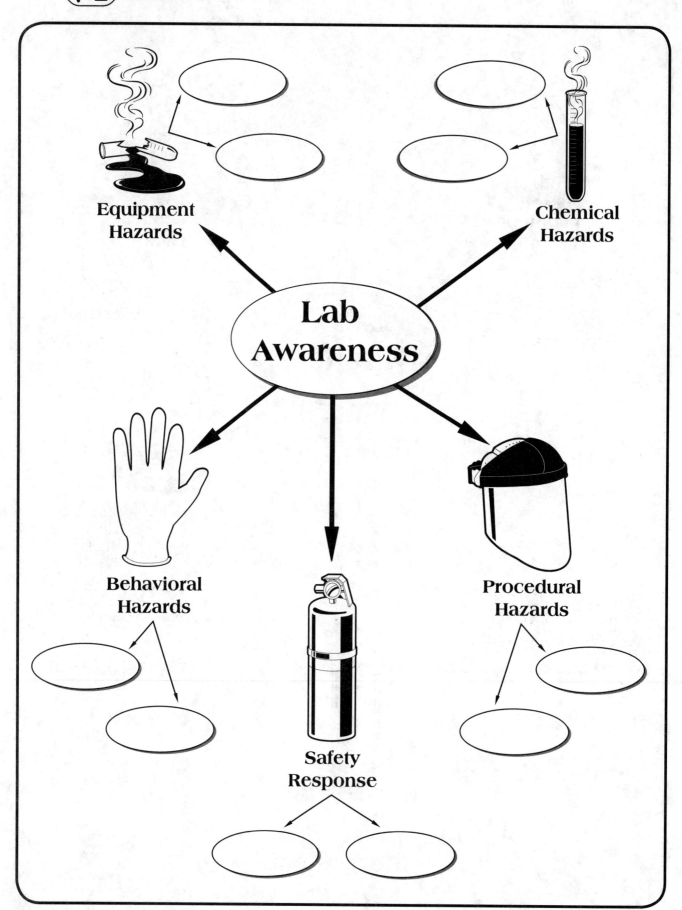

Equipment
Hazards

Chemical
Hazards

Lab
Awareness

Behavioral
Hazards

Safety
Response

Procedural
Hazards

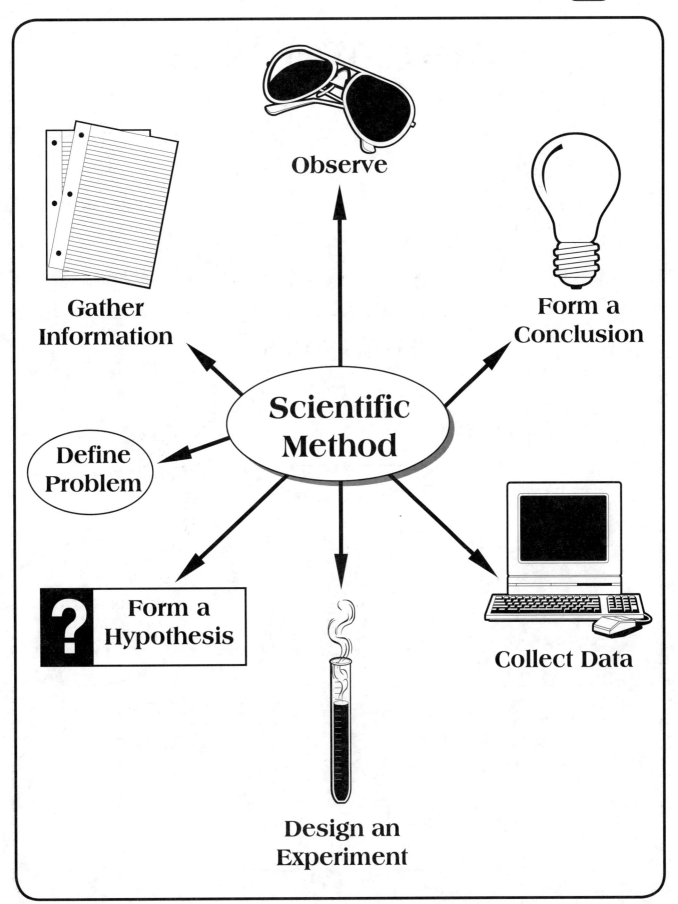

Observe

Gather
Information

Form a
Conclusion

Scientific
Method

Define
Problem

? Form a
Hypothesis

Collect Data

Design an
Experiment

Word Webbing

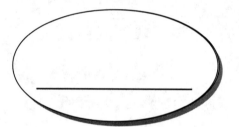

Cooperative Learning Activities For High School Science

PHYSICAL SCIENCE

BIOLOGY

Give One–Get One

ENERAL SCIENCE

CHEMISTRY

EARTH SCIENCE

Give One– Get One

Students circulate in the room, giving and getting ideas.

1 In teams, Students brainstorm Give One items. Pencils down, no writing.

2 When they agree they have come up with a good Give One item, they take up their pencils and each in their own words write it in the Give One column.

3 When their Give One column is full, the team stands.

4 When all teams are standing, each student puts up a hand and moves to find a new partner.

5 In pairs, students each give one idea and get one idea. Students write the idea they received in their own words in the Get One column.

6 Pairs part. Students put a hand up until they find a new partner, and then again give one and get one.

7 When a student's form is full, he/she stands by the perimeter of the room, offering to give one to anyone whose form is not yet full.

8 When all students have finished their forms, they return to their teams and share the ideas they have received.

Student Instructions:
In your teams, brainstorm as many ideas as you can for the topic I give you. When you agree on an idea, write it in the Give One column of your paper. When your column is full, stand up. Then, raise a hand and find a partner. Give your partner an idea, get an idea from your partner, and write it down in the Get One column of your paper. When your form is full, return to your team and share your ideas with your teammates.

Give One–Get One
Activities & Blacklines

Biology

Chemistry

Earth Science

Physical Science

General Science

Give One–Get One
Biology Activity Ideas

1. Bones

Objective: Students will name as many bones and skeletal structures as they can.

Give One	Get One
• Marrow	
• Femur	
• Skull	
• Carpal	

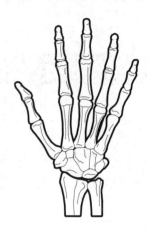

2. Plants

Instructions: Students will identify plant structures and functions.

Give One	Get One
• Cuticle: protective layer	
• Palisades Layer: main photosynthetic area in a leaf	
• Stoma: opening for gas exchange	

3. Tidal Zone Species

Objective: Students will identify tidal zone species as well as where they are found in the water column.

Give One	Get One
• Sea star: benthic	
• Plankton: upper, intertidal	
• Fish: all zones	
• Algae: all photosynthetic zones	

4. Genome Research

Objective: Students will identify examples of how genome research could be used to benefit society; incorporating the ethical issues involved.

Give One	Get One
• Chromosome analysis: useful for genetic disease research and finding possible cures	
• Genetic screening: useful to predict genetic predispositions	

Mammals

Instructions: Name as many members of the class mammalia as you can.

Give One	Get One

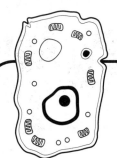

Cellular Organelles

Instructions: Name as many cellular organelles as you can. In column 1 write the name of the organelle, then in column 2 write whether it is found in a plant cell, an animal cell, or both.

Give One		Get One	
Column 1	Column 2	Column 1	Column 2

1. Ionic Compounds

Objective: Students will be able to write the chemical formula for an ionic compound (ex. NaCl) as well as identify the ionic formulas.

Give One	Get One
• Sodium Chloride	
• Calcium Chloride	
• $CaCl_2$	

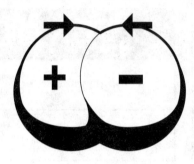

2. Metals

Objective: Students will be able to recognize and name metals as found in the periodic table of the elements.

Give One	Get One
• Calcium	
• Magnesium	
• Zinc	

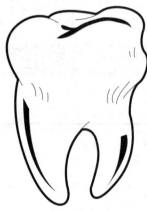

3. Transitional Elements

Objective: Students will be able to identify the transitional elements.

Give One	Get One
• Iron	
• Nickel	
• Platinum	

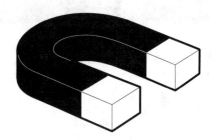

4. Water Pollution

Objective: Students will be able to identify the different factors that contribute to water pollution.

Give One	Get One
• Heavy metal contamination	
• pH	
• Temperature	

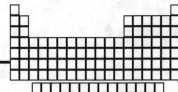

Lewis Dot Structures

Instructions: Draw the Lewis dot structure for as many elements from different groups as you can.

Give One	Get One

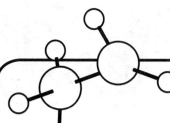

Properties: Chemical or Physical?

Instructions: In column 1, write examples of properties. In column 2, write whether it is an example of a chemical or physical property.

Give One		Get One	
Column 1	Column 2	Column 1	Column 2

Give One–Get One
Earth Science Activity Ideas

1. Sea Floor

Objective: Students will identify the characteristics of the ocean floor.

Give One	Get One
• Hot vents	
• Trench	
• Rift Zone	

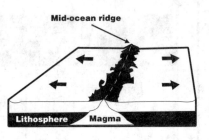

2. Earth's History

Objective: Students will list as many characteristics as they can when comparing the Earth of the past to the Earth of today.

Give One	Get One
• Glacier Prominence	
• Erosion	
• Plate boundaries	

3. Evolution of the Solar System

Objective: Students will identify the process and results of the formation of the solar system.

Give One	Get One
• Big Bang Explosion	
• Jupiter formed	
• Milky Way formed	

4. Conservation

Objective: Students will identify ways to conserve natural resources.

Give One	Get One
• Recycle	
• Use of electric cars	
• Solar panels	

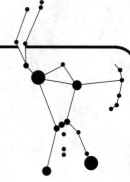

Constellations and Stars

Instructions: Name a constellation or name as many stars as you can.

Give One	Get One

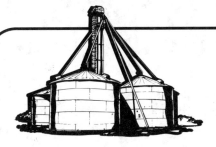

Resources

Instructions: Name as many types of natural resources as you can and next to it say whether it is renewable or nonrenewable.

Give One		Get One	
Resource	(R) renewable (N) nonrenewable	Resource	(R) renewable (N) nonrenewable

1. Scientific Method

Objective: Students will identify a step in the scientific method as well as an example in a particular laboratory setup.

Give One	Get One
• Collect data: measure temperature	
• Form hypothesis: make an if/then statement	
• Analyze data: make a graph	

2. Technology

Objective: Students will name as many technological devices that have impacted the physical world of today as they can.

Give One	Get One
• MRI: medical imaging for diagnosis	
• Computer: used in all types of analysis	
• GPS: used in many earth studies	

3. Acids and Bases

Objective: Students will identify physical and chemical characteristics of acids and bases.

Give One	Get One
• Acid: sour	
• Base: pH 7-14	
• Acid: pH 0-7	

4. Physical Science Application

Objective: Students will identify examples of how physical science concepts are seen in the rides and attractions at an amusement park.

Give One	Get One
• Roller coaster: potential/kinetic energy changes	
• Gravitron: momentum	

Compound Machines

Instructions: What are examples of compound machines found in your home?

Give One	Get One

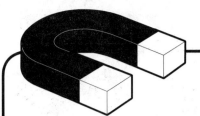

Energy

Instructions: Using your classroom as an example, list as many kinds of kinetic and potential energy as you can in column 1. Put a P for potential or a K for kinetic in column 2 to describe that example.

Give One		Get One	
Column 1 Example	Column 2 K or P	Column 1 Example	Column 2 K or P

GENERAL SCIENCE
BLACKline Give One–Get One

Lab Hazards and Solutions

Instructions: In column 1 name as many lab hazards as you can. In column 2 name the solution to that hazard.

Give One		Get One	
Column 1	Column 2	Column 1	Column 2

PHYSICAL SCIENCE

BIOLOGY

More Science
Structures

ENERAL SCIENCE

CHEMISTRY

EARTH SCIENCE

7 More Science Structures

In this chapter, you will find several other structures that are effective for producing mastery of science content and skills. Depending on the content, some of these structures can also be used for teambuilding, classbuilding, and development of higher level thinking skills. The structures included in this chapter are listed in alphabetical order, and the steps for each of these structures are described in detail.

More Science Structures
Activities & Blacklines

Kagan Publishing • 1 (800) 933-2667
www.KaganOnline.com

Agree-Disagree Line-Ups

Students line up to agree or disagree with a statement, then discuss their positions.

1 Teacher makes a strong statement, taking one side of a controversial issue. For example, "Human cloning should not be permitted."

2 Students line up in proportion to their agreement or disagreement with the statement.

3 Teacher provides an interaction topic. For example, "Why did you take the stance you did?"

4 Students interact in pairs with the student next to them in line, using:
- Timed Pair Share
- RallyRobin

Ideas for using
Agree-Disagree Line-Ups

Biology

- Do you agree or disagree with the use of animals for medical testing?
- Do you agree or disagree with environmental protection laws?
- Do you agree or disagree with species preservation programs?
- Do you agree or disagree with pesticide use?
- Do you agree or disagree with human cloning techniques?
- Do you agree or disagree with genetic screening?
- Do you agree or disagree with using bioengineering in agriculture?

Chemistry

- Do you agree or disagree with the destruction of the environment to obtain fossil fuels?
- Do you agree or disagree that the risk of petroleum spills in the ocean is worth the risk to the environment?
- Do you agree or disagree that the use of fossil fuels should be limited?
- Do you agree or disagree with research in chemical warfare?
- Do you agree or disagree that alternative energy vehicles should be mandated in heavily populated cities?

Ideas for using
Agree-Disagree Line-Ups

Earth Science
- Do you agree or disagree with strip mining?
- Do you agree or disagree with man-made vs. natural gems being considered equal?
- Do you agree or disagree with exploring space and the oceans as means of getting rid of garbage?
- Do you agree or disagree that living forms exist on other planets?

Physical Science
- The steps for solving an equation. (For example: The first step in solving this equation is finding the variables.)
- The answer to the problem. (For example: The answer to this problem is 1.04×10^3.)
- Do you agree or disagree with limiting the production and use of products that contain CFCs that may lead to global warming?
- Predictions for physical results in nature. (For example: A penny and a book dropped from the Sear's tower will hit the Earth at the same time.)
- Do you agree or disagree that solar energy research should become a priority?

General Science
- Laboratory Procedures (For example: When using a razor blade, make the cut toward your body.)
- Laboratory Hypothesis and Predictions (For example: I predict that solution A is a base.)
- Laboratory Results/Conclusions (For example: Based on the data collected, isopods respond to light.)

Genetic Engineering

Instructions: Each of the following open-ended questions is an excellent opening discussion topic for a unit on genetics, society, and biology. These questions should be read to the class and then used as the topic for a value line up. The value line up for agree/disagree can be folded or shifted so that the same opinion can be shared or so that differing opinions can be shared between partners.

1. **Do you agree or disagree:** Stem cell research should be legal in the United States?

2. **Do you agree or disagree:** Creating genetically modified food crops is an acceptable use of biotechnology?

3. **Do you agree or disagree:** It is okay to genetically modify an unborn fetus?

4. **Do you agree or disagree:** The government should fund scientific research?

5. **Do you agree or disagree:** Human cloning should be permitted?

6. **Do you agree or disagree:** The results from the Human Genome Project should be sold for profit?

7. **Do you agree or disagree:** Using genetically engineered bacteria that protect crops from insect damage should be allowed; and therefore, such bacteria should be released into the environment?

8. **Do you agree or disagree:** Insurance companies should have the right to genetically screen future clients?

9. **Do you agree or disagree:** The FBI and other law enforcement agencies should have the right to create DNA profiles on individuals?

10. **Do you agree or disagree:** DNA manipulation should be used to recreate extinct organisms?

Nuclear Energy

Instructions: Each of the following open-ended questions is an excellent opening discussion topic for a unit on nuclear energy. These questions should be read to the class and then used as the topic for Agree-Disagree Line-Ups. The line can be folded or shifted so that the same opinion can be shared or so that differing opinions can be shared between partners.

1. **Do you agree or disagree:** Nuclear energy should be our major source of electricity?

2. **Do you agree or disagree:** There should be a ban on nuclear arms?

3. **Do you agree or disagree:** Yucca Mountain is an ideal place to dispose of nuclear waste?

4. **Do you agree or disagree:** The government should destroy all stored nuclear warheads?

5. **Do you agree or disagree:** The atmosphere should be monitored for nuclear contaminants?

6. **Do you agree or disagree:** People living near nuclear power plants are crazy?

7. **Do you agree or disagree:** We should attack unfriendly countries developing nuclear arms before they get them and it's too late?

8. **Do you agree or disagree:** Nuclear war will one day blow up the Earth?

9. **Do you agree or disagree:** Nuclear weapons are a bad thing?

10. **Do you agree or disagree:** We should test the effects of radiation on animals?

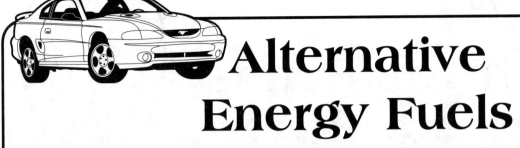

Alternative Energy Fuels

Instructions: Each of the following open-ended questions is an excellent opening discussion topic for a unit on alternative energy fuels. These questions should be read to the class and then used as the topic for Agree-Disagree Line-Ups. The line can be folded or shifted so that the same opinion can be shared or so that differing opinions can be shared between partners.

1. **Do you agree or disagree:** Alternative energy vehicles should be mandated in heavily populated cities?

2. **Do you agree or disagree:** SUVs and other gas-guzzling vehicles should be charged an extra fuel tax?

3. **Do you agree or disagree:** People who purchase electric cars or hybrids should get a tax break?

4. **Do you agree or disagree:** The government should sponsor scientists to investigate alternative energy sources?

5. **Do you agree or disagree:** People should have a limit as to how much gas they can use in their houses?

6. **Do you agree or disagree:** Solar panels should be installed in all new houses?

7. **Do you agree or disagree:** Fossil fuels will eventually run out?

Alien Life Forms

Instructions: Each of the following open-ended questions is an excellent opening discussion topic for a unit on space or alien life forms. These questions should be read to the class and then used as the topic for Agree-Disagree Line-Ups. The line can be folded or shifted so that the same opinion can be shared or so that differing opinions can be shared between partners.

1. **Do you agree or disagree:** Living forms exist on other planets?

2. **Do you agree or disagree:** There might be plants on other planets, but definitely not animal life?

3. **Do you agree or disagree:** Alien abductions are real?

4. **Do you agree or disagree:** The government is keeping alien information from people because people couldn't handle the reality?

5. **Do you agree or disagree:** If extraterrestrial life exists, it is much less sophisticated than humans?

6. **Do you agree or disagree:** Space travel will soon be within the reach of the general population?

7. **Do you agree or disagree:** The space program is nowhere as important as the government dealing with our problems here on Earth?

8. **Do you agree or disagree:** The existence of bacteria on other planets would be proof of alien life forms?

Fan-N-Pick

Students play a card game to respond to questions.

1 Student One holds question cards in a fan and says "Pick a card, any card!"

2 Student Two picks a card, reads the question out loud and allows five seconds of think time.

3 Student Three answers the question.

4 Student Four responds to the answer:
- For right or wrong answers, Student Four checks and then either praises or tutors.
- For higher-level thinking questions which have no right or wrong answer, Student Four does not check for correctness but paraphrases and praises the thinking that went into the answer.

5 Students rotate roles one clockwise for each new round.

Origins of Life

Instructions: Teacher prepares review questions on cards. Team captain fans cards. Student Two picks a card and reads it. Student Three answers the question. Student Four thanks and praises. Next person becomes the new team captain.

1 What are the three gasses believed to be the forerunners of life on Earth?

2 What was the energy source that changed the chemistry of the early Earth?

3 What evidence do we have that indicates what early Earth was like?

4 Could life have been supported on early Earth? Why or why not?

5 What is one theory about the origins of life on early Earth?

6 What is another theory about the origins of life on early Earth?

Origins of Life

7 What were the first cells on the early Earth like?

8 What is the significance of the onset of photosynthesis on the early Earth?

9 How did cells change once photosynthesis occurred?

10 What do fossils tell us about the early Earth?

11 How did life change when multicellular organisms arose?

12 What is meant by division of labor in cells?

 Fan·N·Pick

Periodic Table

Instructions: Teacher prepares review questions on cards. Team captain fans cards. Student Two picks a card and reads it. Student Three answers the question. Student Four thanks and praises. Next person becomes the new team captain.

1 How many outer shell electrons are in the Ca atom?	**2** How many energy levels are in the K atom?
3 What is one element that has a -1 charge?	**4** What is one noble gas?
5 Which is more reactive, F or Br?	**6** Which is more reactive, Na or K?
7 Which is more reactive, Na or Ca?	**8** What is one transitional element from the third period?

Periodic Table

9 What is one element that will bond with Cl and result in a formula with no subscripts?

10 What are the subscripts needed to satisfy the elements in a compound made of Al and O?

11 What is one element that is a halogen?

12 What is one element that is a metalloid?

13 What is the subscript for Na if it bonds with N?

14 What is an element that will bond with Cl and will require a subscript of 2 for the Cl?

15 What is one alkali metal?

16 Where are the strongest metals found?

EARTH SCIENCE
BLACKline Fan-N-Pick

Geologic Time

Instructions: Teacher prepares review questions on cards. Team captain fans cards. Student Two picks a card and reads it. Student Three answers the question. Student Four thanks and praises. Next person becomes the new team captain.

1 What is the geologic time scale?

2 What is the era and the time period that corresponds to it?

3 What happened during the Pliocene Epoch?

4 How is a fossil formed?

5 What is the principle of superposition?

6 How does radioactive decay tell you how old something is?

Geologic Time

7 What is the half-life of carbon-14?

8 What does uranium-238 break down into?

9 What is the difference between relative-age dating and absolute-age dating?

10 Potassium-40 decays into the noble gas argon-40. What is one problem that could occur when trying to date a sample that has broken down in this fashion?

Magnetism

Instructions: Teacher prepares review questions on cards. Team captain fans cards. Student Two picks a card and reads it. Student Three answers the question. Student Four thanks and praises. Next person becomes the new team captain.

1 What is another name for magnetite?

2 How can you describe the magnetic field that surrounds a bar magnet (or draw it)?

3 How can you make a temporary magnet?

4 How does the Earth act like a magnet?

Magnetism

5 How does a compass work?

6 Why is the following statement true: The Earth's magnetic north pole is near the Earth's geographic south pole?

7 In what country is the Earth's magnetic south pole?

8 What metal is the inner core of the Earth composed of?

Mix-Freeze-Group

Students rush to form groups of a specific size, hoping not to land in "Lost and Found."

1 Students "mix" around the room.

2 Teacher calls, "Freeze."

3 Students freeze.

4 Teacher asks a question to which the answer is a number or corresponds to a key with a number. (Examples: How many planets are there in our solar system? What macromolecule is the following food?
Key: 1 = Carbohydrate, 2 = Lipid, 3 = Protein, 4 = Nucleic Acid.)

5 Students group according to the number, and kneel down.

6 Students not in groups go to the "Lost and Found."

Optional: Once students know the game, students in Lost and Found may be the ones to generate and ask the question. After they ask the question they rush to join a group.

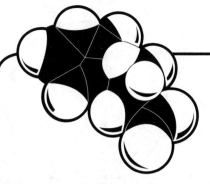

Bond Sites

Instructions: Students mix around the room. Teacher calls, "freeze" and poses a question that requires a number answer. Students group to reflect on the answer. If the answer requires a positive sign, students face the center of the circle. If the answer requires a negative sign, students group with their backs to the circle.

The soupy sea of elements provides the early Earth environment with four basic elements that were chemically compatible because of their bond sites.

1. How many bond sites are there in the element C?

2. How many bond sites are there in the element N?

3. How many bond sites are there in the element H?

4. How many bond sites are there in the element O?

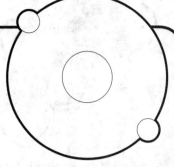

Atomic Charge

Instructions: Students mix around the room. Teacher calls, "freeze" and poses a question that requires a number answer. Students group to reflect on the answer. If the answer requires a positive sign, students face the center of the circle. If the answer requires a negative sign, students group with their backs to the circle.

1. What is the charge of O?

2. What is the charge of N?

3. How many energy levels are there in an I atom?

4. How many protons does a He atom have?

5. If the atomic mass of Li is 7 and the atomic number is 3, how many neutrons does it have?

6. How many electrons are present in the outer shell of the noble gas, radon?

Earth's Technological Measurements

Instructions: Students mix around the room. Teacher calls, "freeze" and poses a question that requires a number answer. Students group to reflect on the answer. If the answer requires a positive sign, students face the center of the circle. If the answer requires a negative sign, students group with their backs to the circle.

1. What is the highest storm rating of a tornado?

2. What is the highest rating on the Richter Scale?

3. What is the force exerted due to a hurricane if the mass of the falling object is 8 g?

4. What is the speed of a wave in a storm that has a frequency of 4 hertz and a wavelength of 8 meters?

Astronomy

Instructions: Students mix around the room. Teacher calls, "freeze" and poses a question that requires a number answer. Students group to reflect on the answer. If the answer requires a positive sign, students face the center of the circle. If the answer requires a negative sign, students group with their backs to the circle.

1. How many planets are there?

2. How many moons does the Earth have?

3. How many moons are around Saturn?

4. How many stars make up the constellation Orion?

5. How many phases are there in the Moon's cycle?

6. At what position is the Earth in relation to the sun?

7. What position is Neptune to Earth?

Numbered Heads Together

Teammates work together to ensure all members understand; one is randomly selected to be held accountable.

1 Students number off.

2 Teacher poses a problem and gives think time. (Example: "Everyone think about how rainbows are formed". Pause "Now write your own answer.")

3 Students get up from their chairs to put their heads together, discuss and teach.

4 Students sit down when everyone knows the answer or has something to share.

5 Teacher calls a number. The student with that number from each team answers simultaneously, using:
- Slate Share
- Choral Practice
- Finger Responses
- Chalkboard Responses
- Response Cards
- Manipulatives

6 Teammates praise students who responded.

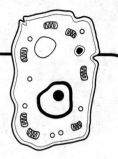

Life

Instructions: While in student groups, teacher poses a question to the class. Group huddles until they all know the answer. Teacher calls on one number to respond.

1. What are three ways you can distinguish between living and nonliving things?

2. What are three organic molecules that are present in living cells?

3. What are two chemical activities that are necessary to maintain all living things?

4. How did Redi's experiment disprove spontaneous generation?

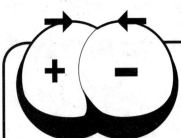

Ions

Instructions: While in student groups, teacher poses a question to the class. Group huddles until they all know the answer. Teacher calls on one number to respond.

1. What is the difference between ionization and electron affinity?

2. Describe how a positive ion is formed.

3. Is the positive ion larger or smaller than its atom and why?

4. Describe how a negative ion is formed.

5. Is a negative ion larger or smaller than its atom and why?

Kagan Publishing • 1 (800) 933-2667
www.KaganOnline.com

Sequencing

This simple structure can be used with a wide range of content — almost anything that has an ordinal sequence.

1 Cards are dealt out, at least one per student.

2 Student One turns one of his or her cards face up and states where in the sequence it belongs.

3 All students discuss. If adjustments need to be made, only Student One may move the card.

4 Repeat steps 2 and 3 for each student in turn, until all cards are placed.

5 Students check sequence for correctness and celebrate.

Ideas for using
Sequencing

Biology
- Steps in digestion process
- Reactions of photosynthesis
- Steps of protein synthesis
- Steps in DNA replication
- Tracing fossil "evolution"
- Steps in forming the first cell

Chemistry
- Steps in obtaining petroleum
- Steps in balancing a chemical equation
- Steps in setting up a chemical lab experiment (works for any lab procedure)
- Steps in purifying water
- Steps in fractional distillation
- Steps in writing formulas

Earth Science
- Steps in hurricane formation
- Steps involved in forming a diamond
- Steps in the formation of the universe
- Steps in forming a fossil
- Steps involved in determining half-life

Physical Science
- Steps in solving an equation
- Steps in forming a solution
- Steps that occur when water changes states
- Steps in determining the density of a regular solid

Cell Life Cycle

Interphase	**Prophase**
Metaphase	**Anaphase**

Cooperative Learning Activities For High School Science

Cell Life Cycle

Telophase

Cytokinesis

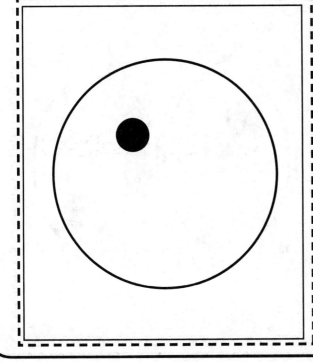

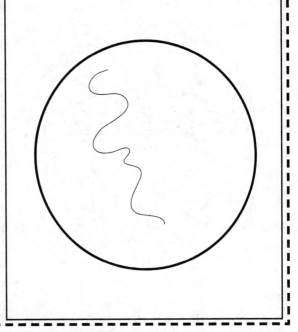

Cell Life Cycle

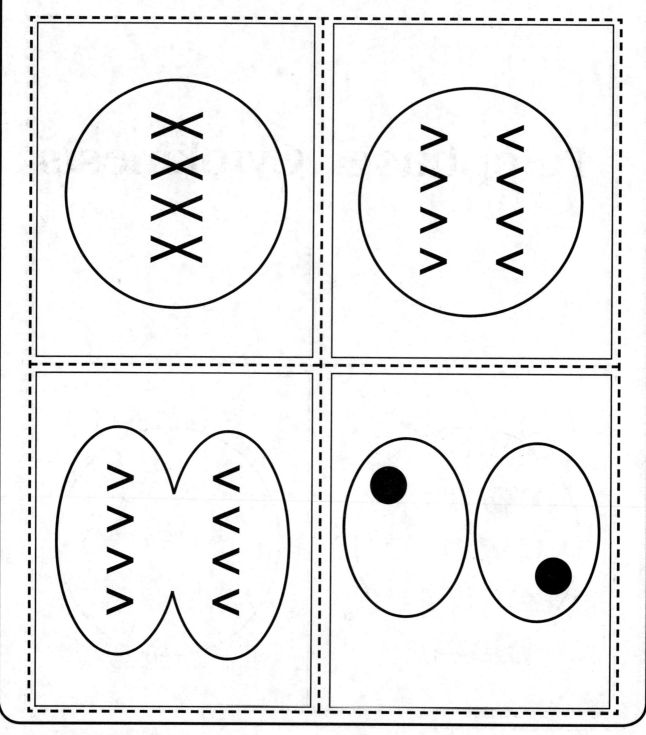

Fractions of Distillation Based on Temperature

Crude oil	**Gaseous product**
Gaseous products used to manufacture plastic	**Liquid products used to make gasoline**

Kagan Publishing • 1 (800) 933-2667
www.KaganOnline.com

Fractions of Distillation Based on Temperature

Liquid products used as solvents	Liquid products used as fuels
Liquid products used as lubricating oils	Heavy residue used as waxes

Steps in the Evolution of Earth's Geological History

Tertiary

Cretaceous

Jurassic

Triassic

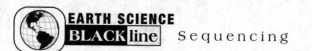

Steps in the Evolution of Earth's Geological History

Permian

Pennsylvanian

Mississippian

Devonian

Steps in the Evolution of Earth's Geological History

Silurian

Ordovician

Cambrian

Precambrian

Steps Involved in Constructing a Graph

Set up X and Y axes

Determine range for each variable

Label each axis

Plot data

Steps Involved in Constructing a Graph

Connect data points

Determine slope

Draw a trend line

Construct a key

Sequencing Blank Cards Template

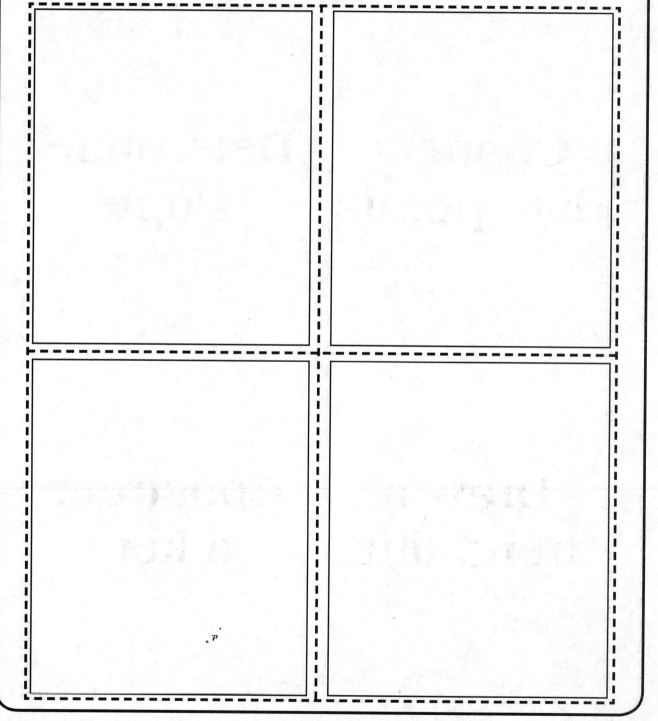

Showdown

Students answer questions without help.
Teams then check and coach.

1 Question cards are stacked in the center of the team table.

2 Teacher selects one student on each team to be the showdown captain for the first round. Showdown captain draws the top card and reads the question.

3 Working alone, all students write their answers.

4 When finished, teammates signal they're ready.

5 The showdown captain calls "showdown."

6 Teammates show answers; showdown captain leads checking.

7 If correct, the team celebrates; if not, teammates coach, then celebrate.

8 The person on left of the showdown captain becomes the new showdown captain for the next round (repeat from Step 2).

BIOLOGY
BLACKline Showdown

Cellular Organization

Instructions: Showdown captain draws a card and reads the question to teammates. Students independently answer the question. Showdown captain calls, "showdown," and all teammates show their answers.

1 What is the name of the control center of the cell?

2 What is a nucleated cell called?

3 What is a non-nucleated cell called?

4 What is the roadway inside the cell called?

5 What does the lysosome do?

6 What does the vacuole do?

Cellular Organization

7 What controls movement into and out of the cell?

8 What provides rigidity and support to a plant cell?

9 What organelle holds the chlorophyll?

10 What organelle holds the DNA?

11 What do the Golgi bodies do?

12 What is the jelly like substance in a cell called?

History of the Periodic Table

Instructions: Questions should be used after reading a biographical article on Mendeleyev.

1 Where was Mendeleyev born?	**2** What year was Mendeleyev born?
3 What school subjects were his favorites?	**4** What happened when Mendeleyev got his first job and why?
5 When did he begin his scientific research?	**6** What were the two things that Mendeleyev began to relate while studying chemistry?

History of the Periodic Table

7 While traveling on scientific assignments, what scientific activities was Mendeleyev directly involved in?

8 What social conditions of his time was he interested in?

9 What did Mendeleyev observe about the relationship between atomic mass and the elements?

10 What did Mendeleyev do when he played "chemical solitaire"?

11 What predictions did Mendeleyev make as a result of his studies?

12 Why did the chemical community ostracize Mendeleyev?

Kagan Publishing • 1 (800) 933-2667
www.KaganOnline.com

EARTH SCIENCE
BLACKline S h o w d o w n

Mapping

Instructions: Showdown captain draws a card and reads the question to teammates. Students independently answer the question. Showdown captain calls, "showdown," and all teammates show their answers.

---

1 What is the difference between latitude and longitude?

2 What does the prime meridian represent?

3 What is a country that the prime meridian goes through?

4 What is the name of the line that runs horizontally halfway between the north and south poles?

5 In what ocean is the international dateline located?

6 What degree of longitude is the international dateline?

Mapping

7 If it is 3:00 PM in New Jersey (EST), what time is it in Oklahoma (CST) and Oregon (PST)?

8 What does GPS stand for?

9 How does GPS work?

10 What does sonar mean?

11 How does sonar work?

12 What type of map shows changes in elevation?

Forces

Instructions: Showdown captain draws a card and reads the question to teammates. Students independently answer the question. Showdown captain calls, "showdown," and all teammates show their answers.

1 What is the definition of a force?

2 What are unbalanced forces and how do they relate to motion?

3 What is the one result that occurs from friction?

4 Which of Newton's laws makes the space shuttle fly and why?

5 How can Newton's first law be seen while driving a car?

6 What is the equation for Newton's second law of motion?

Forces

7 What constant is the acceleration due to the force of gravity?

8 How does air resistance effect the motion of a falling object?

9 Name one thing that will increase the gravitational attraction between two objects.

10

11

12

Telephone

One student per team leaves the room during instruction. When students return, teammates provide instruction in the information missed.

1 One student from each team ("the learner") is selected to leave the room.

2 Remaining students ("the teachers") receive instruction.

3 The teachers plan how best to instruct the learner and who will teach each part—each takes a part of the teaching.

4 Learners return to their teams.

5 The teachers each teach their part of the content (RoundRobin); teammates augment as necessary.

6 The learners take a practice test.

The sample content on the following page is divided into four topics. Teammates can each take responsibility for teaching the learner one of the topics.

Here are two variations to Telephone:

- **Jigsaw** Each student is assigned one of the four topics. They become experts on their topics. They return to their teams to teach their teammates what they learned about the topic.
- **Learner Topic Telephone** The learner who leaves the room is given one of the topics to master. When he/she returns, he/she teaches teammates what he/she learned about the assigned topic. Teammates then teach The learner about the other topics.

Ideas for using
Telephone

Biology

Cell Processes
- **Topic 1:** Mitosis
- **Topic 2:** Meiosis
- **Topic 3:** DNA transcription
- **Topic 4:** DNA replication

Chemistry

Families of the Periodic Table
- **Topic 1:** Halogens
- **Topic 2:** Noble gases
- **Topic 3:** Alkali metals
- **Topic 4:** Alkaline Earth metals

Conservation
- **Topic 1:** Renewable resources
- **Topic 2:** Nonrenewable resources
- **Topic 3:** Recycling
- **Topic 4:** Conservation

Lab On Separation
- **Topic 1:** Paper filtration
- **Topic 2:** Sand filtration
- **Topic 3:** Charcoal separation
- **Topic 4:** Distillation

Earth Science

Natural Disasters
- **Topic 1:** Earthquakes
- **Topic 2:** Volcanoes
- **Topic 3:** Hurricanes
- **Topic 4:** Tornadoes

Kagan Publishing • 1 (800) 933-2667
www.KaganOnline.com

Ideas for using
Telephone

Physical Science

Waves
- **Topic 1:** Waves
- **Topic 2:** Reflection
- **Topic 3:** Refraction
- **Topic 4:** Diffraction

General Science

Introduction to
Lab Procedures
- **Topic 1:** Safety
- **Topic 2:** Lab procedures
- **Topic 3:** Equipment
- **Topic 4:** Class rules/group rules

Timed Pair Share

In pairs, students share with a partner for a predetermined time while the partner listens carefully. Then partners switch roles.

1 Teacher announces a topic and states how long each student will have to share.

2 Teacher provides think time.

3 In pairs, Partner A shares; Partner B listens.

4 Partner B responds. (Example: "Thanks for sharing. One thing I learned as I listened to you was…")

5 Pairs switch roles: Partner B shares; Partner A listens.

6 Partner A responds.

Life and Change

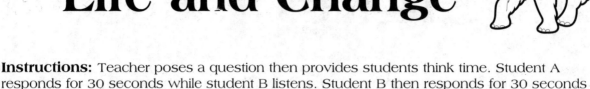

Instructions: Teacher poses a question then provides students think time. Student A responds for 30 seconds while student B listens. Student B then responds for 30 seconds while student A listens.

1. What are some factors that are changing the life span of humans?

2. Why are so many species becoming extinct?

3. What did sexual reproduction do to enhance the process of evolution?

4. What are some stimulus responses that help to protect you, and how do they do that?

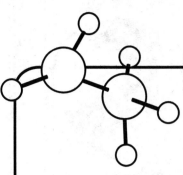

Discussing Bonds

Instructions: Teacher poses a question then provides students think time. Student A responds for 30 seconds while student B listens. Student B then responds for 30 seconds while student A listens.

1. **Partner A** What is energy's involvement in the formation of covalent bonds?
   Partner B What is energy's involvement in the formation of ionic bonds?

2. What are the differences between molecules and crystals?

3. **Partner A** What are three examples of elements that will form covalent bonds?
   Partner B What are three examples of elements that will form ionic bonds?

EARTH SCIENCE BLACKline Timed Pair Share

Weather

Instructions: Teacher poses a question then provides students think time. Student A responds for 30 seconds while student B listens. Student B then responds for 30 seconds while student A listens.

1. What kinds of aid is administered to devastated areas due to weather?

2. What types of damage occur from extreme weather patterns?

3. If weather patterns could not be predicted with such accuracy, how would your daily life be affected?

4. Economically, why is weather prediction important?

Pollution

Instructions: Teacher poses a question then provides students think time. Student A responds for 30 seconds while student B listens. Student B then responds for 30 seconds while student A listens.

1. What are some of the ecological impacts of an oil spill?

2. What remedies can be used to clean up and remediate the site?

3. What preventative measures could be taken to prevent an oil spill?

4. What laws could be enacted to protect the environment?

Notes

Notes

Notes

Notes

Kagan Publishing • 1 (800) 933-2667
www.KaganOnline.com

Notes

Kagan

It's All About Engagement!

Kagan is the world leader **in creating active engagement in the classroom.** Learn how to engage your students and you will boost achievement, prevent discipline problems, and make learning more fun and meaningful. Come join Kagan for a workshop or call Kagan to **set up a workshop for your school or district**. Experience the power of a Kagan workshop. **Experience the engagement!**

SPECIALIZING IN:

★ **Cooperative Learning**

★ **Win-Win Discipline**

★ **Brain-Friendly Teaching**

★ **Multiple Intelligences**

★ **Thinking Skills**

★ **Kagan Coaching**

KAGAN PROFESSIONAL DEVELOPMENT

www.KaganOnline.com ★ 1(800) 266-7576

It's All About Engagement!

**Kagan is your source
for active engagement in the classroom.**

Check out Kagan's line of books, smartcards, software, electronics, and hands-on learning resources all designed to boost engagement in your classroom.

Books

SmartCards

Spinners

Learning Chips

Posters

Learning Cubes

KAGAN PUBLISHING

www.KaganOnline.com ★ 1(800) 933-2667